MEN OF DIALOGUE: Martin Buber and Albrecht Goes

MARTIN BUBER

ALBRECHT GOES

Men of Dialogue:

MARTIN BUBER AND ALBRECHT GOES

EDITED BY E. WILLIAM ROLLINS & HARRY ZOHN

Preface by Maurice Friedman

FUNK & WAGNALLS, NEW YORK

The editors wish to acknowledge the kind permission of the following publishers, translators, and individuals to publish material for which they hold copyrights:

A section of "My Way to Hasidism" from *Hasidism and Modern Man* by Martin Buber, edited and translated by Maurice Friedman, copyright 1958 by Martin Buber; a quotation from "Guilt and Guilt Feelings" from *The Knowledge of Man* by Martin Buber, translated by Maurice Friedman, copyright 1965 by Martin Buber and Maurice Friedman; "What Is To Be Done?" and "Genuine Dialogue and the Possibilities of Peace" from *Pointing the Way* by Martin Buber, translated by Maurice Friedman, copyright 1957 by Martin Buber and 1963 by Maurice Friedman; all by permission of Harper & Row.

"Second Response" from "Church, State, Nation, Jewry" by Martin Buber, translated by William Hallo, from *Christianity: Some Non-Christian Appraisals,* edited by David McKain, copyright 1964, by permission of the publisher, McGraw-Hill Book Company.

Unquiet Night by Albrecht Goes, translated by Constantine Fitzgibbon, copyright 1951, by permission of Michael Joseph, Ltd.

The Burnt Offering by Albrecht Goes, translated by Michael Hamburger, copyright 1956 by Pantheon Books, Inc., by permission of Random House, Inc.

"Encounter in Hungary" ("Begegnung in Ungarn"), "Judgment and Prejudice" ("Urteil und Vorurteil"), "The *Deluxe* Dress Material" ("Der schwere Herrenstoff"), "Go, Suffer, Wait" ("Gehe, leide, warte"), from *Aber im Winde das Wort* by Albrecht Goes, copyright 1963 by G. B. Fischer and Co.; *The Boychik* (original title *Das Löffelchen*), copyright 1965 by S. Fischer Verlag; "Martin Buber, Our Support" ("Martin Buber der Beistand"), from *Ruf und Echo,* copyright 1956 by S. Fischer Verlag, GmbH; all by permission of S. Fischer Verlag.

THE LIFE OF DIALOGUE IS NOT ONE IN WHICH
YOU HAVE MUCH TO DO WITH MEN, BUT ONE IN
WHICH YOU REALLY HAVE TO DO WITH THOSE
WITH WHOM YOU HAVE TO DO.

—Martin Buber, *Dialogue*

PREFACE

IN 1961 HARRY KAHN, PROFESSOR OF GERMAN AT THE UNIVERSITY
of Vermont, gave me Albrecht Goes's beautiful little novel
Unruhige Nacht (*Unquiet Night*) and suggested that I find
a publisher who would bring out a number of Goes's works
that are, like this one, in the spirit of Martin Buber and the
"life of dialogue." Since then this idea grew on me, so that
when in 1966 Professors Zohn and Rollins told me of their
plan for a book centered on the meeting of Buber and Goes, I
gladly acted the role of middleman and put them in touch
with my friend Roger Donald of Funk & Wagnalls. The book
that has resulted is made up of diverse kinds and lengths of
selections. Yet *Men of Dialogue* has a rare unity of spirit that
will lay hold of many readers in a deeply personal way.

My first "meeting" with Albrecht Goes was when I read the
remarkable address that he gave in Frankfurt-am-Main, Germany, in September, 1953. There Martin Buber, despite the
unanimous criticism of the Israeli and Yiddish press, accepted
the Peace Prize of the German Book Trade that had been
given only twice before—to Albert Schweitzer and Romano
Guardini. Goes's address was called "Martin Buber: Our Sup-

port," and there could have been no deeper or more moving confirmation of the rightness of the decision of this "arch-Jew" (the name that the leading Nazis gave Buber) to fight for the human within the German people against the anti-human that opposes it. Albrecht Goes has never forgotten and has never let his fellow Germans forget that extermination of six million Jews that Buber in his Peace Prize address described as "a systematically prepared and executed procedure whose organized cruelty cannot be compared with any previous historical event." At the time of the *Fragebogen*,[1] when the Neo-Nazis were arising in post-World War II Germany and depreciating the extent of the holocaust as being "merely a million," Goes's novel *The Burnt Offering* stood as the very symbol of the human which Buber had sought to strengthen within the German people.

In the spring of 1960 Buber gave me in Jerusalem another essay on him by Albrecht Goes, "A Living Legend"—a portrait that impressed me as deeply in its way as the earlier one. A few months later I met Goes himself at a reception given for Buber by the Academy of Fine Arts in Munich after his lecture on "The Word That Is Spoken." Goes was tall, strong, composed, gentle, humorous—a man of presence and of spirit, worthy indeed of being Martin Buber's partner in dialogue across the gulf between Christianity and Judaism and the abyss between a chaplain in Hitler's army and a Jew who, systematically deprived of every possibility of activity or help to his fellow Jews, finally left Germany in 1938 to live and die in the Land of Israel. Since then everything that I have read by Goes, whether novel, essay, or letter, has shown how deeply he has made "the life of dialogue" his own.

---

[1] The *Fragebogen* were the de-Nazification questionnaires put out by the American military government in West Germany. In 1951 a leading German press, Rowohlt Verlag, Hamburg, published a voluminous autobiographical (?) novel using the questions of the questionnaire as its framework. From March 1951, to August 1952, the book went through eight printings and sold 206,000 copies. The book was *Der Fragebogen* by Ernst von Salomon.

The subtitle of *Men of Dialogue* might seem misleading since most of the material in the book is by Goes. Yet genuine dialogue also includes Goes's wholehearted response to Buber, the "support," who strengthened and comforted through his works, even apart from the personal relationship that later developed between the two men. Another German writer found strength to endure Nazi torture through thinking of the sufferings borne by the poor Jews in Buber's *Tales of the Hasidim* and insisting to himself that he, an aristocratic Junker, should be able to do the same!

In the Selected Bibliography Professor Rollins lists my forthcoming biography *Martin Buber: Encounter on the Narrow Ridge* and comments, "One of Buber's encounters on the narrow ridge was that with Albrecht Goes." Actually, the meeting between Buber and Goes was a great deal more than that. It was a high point of Buber's most awesome and terrible "encounter on the narrow ridge" and as such belongs to the most important section of my second volume—his encounter with Nazism. Both Buber and Goes are true "men of dialogue." Many of the Goes selections in this book, such as the tender and painful conversation in *Unquiet Night* between the chaplain and the soldier condemned to be shot, or the emphasis upon understanding the "other" in "Judgment and Prejudice," spring from the very heart of real dialogue. Yet genuine dialogue takes place in situation, in "the lived concrete," and the lived concrete for both men was the confrontation with Nazi Germany. The dialogue between Goes and Buber is a dialogue with each other in response to this unimaginably terrible sequence of events.

Although Goes was never among the procession of German Christians who came to Israel to see Buber during the last fifteen years of his life, it is Goes above all who represents and embodies the German-Christian conscience in its search for an honest way to acknowledge *its* guilt toward the millions of Jews exterminated by the Nazis. When Buber received the Peace Prize of the German Book Trade, he declared that he had "only in a formal sense a common humanity with those who took part in this action": "They have so radically . . . transposed themselves into a sphere of monstrous inhumanity inaccessible to my conception, that not even hatred, much less an overcoming of hatred, was able to arise in me." But Buber also spoke of others who heard rumors and could not bring themselves to investigate, and finally of those who suffered death rather than take part in what was going on. Frau Walker, in Goes's novel *The Burnt Offering*, is one of these last—a German who would rather die than go along with what was happening.

Buber's plea to Ben-Gurion to stay the execution of Adolf Eichmann was based not only on Buber's opposition to capital punishment, but also on his concern for the education of the generation of young Germans who needed to live with the guilt of their fathers and who might take Eichmann's execution as a symbolic expiation. No one has done more than Albrecht Goes to keep the young generation of Germans aware of and willing to shoulder responsibility for their nation's guilt in destroying the foundation of common human existence. Every selection by Goes in this book has as its core the real guilt of the concrete, historical situation. It does not reduce this guilt to neurotic guilt feelings or excuse it as the fault of the leaders only or abstract it into a theological sinfulness that applies to everybody and nobody. If the assassination of the great German-Jewish statesman Walther Rathenau was a presage of the Nazi "final solution" of the "Jewish question," the boy Goes's response to the letter from Rathenau's mother to the mother of her son's assassin was the beginning of his own life-path in illuminating his and his people's existential guilt, persevering in that illumination, and repairing, where he could, the injured order of existence.[2] Real guilt means the breaking off of dialogue between man and man and the over-

[2] I use the language of "Guilt and Guilt Feelings," my translation, in Martin Buber, *The Knowledge of Man*, edited with an Introductory Essay by Maurice Friedman (New York: Harper Torchbooks, 1966).

coming of guilt its resumption. "All real living is meeting," says Martin Buber, and Albrecht Goes confirms: "It is for question and answer that we come up against one another on our way."

MAURICE FRIEDMAN
Temple University
December, 1968

CONTENTS

THREE NOVELS OF EXPIATION

PERSONAL ENCOUNTERS WITH MARTIN BUBER

INTRODUCTION

THIS BOOK IS BY AND ABOUT TWO "MEN OF DIALOGUE" WHO EN-
countered each other on a narrow ridge and, in a spirit of ecu-
menism, essayed a handshake across an abyss. Martin Buber,
known to the English-speaking public through well over thirty
books by him and a number of studies about him currently in
print, has been called the most important Jewish thinker of
the twentieth century. His philosophy of dialogue and his interpretations of Hasidism have earned him a permanent place
among those great writers whose works span not only races and
nations but all academic disciplines. The present volume includes several of his essays not previously published in English
and brings out a new dimension of his "I and Thou" philosophy by showing a specific application of it by a contemporary
German Protestant pastor and man of letters.

Albrecht Goes (the "oe" in his name is pronounced like the
"oe" in Goethe) was a chaplain in Hitler's army, serving in
prisons and hospitals. The fact that Hitler allowed chaplains
will surprise many readers, and what such a man has to say
about the Nazis, the Jews, and his own feelings and opinions
about man's guilt in general and Germany's in particular re-

flect the validity and relevance of Buber's thought where it may be least expected. Goes's short novel *Unquiet Night* was first published in English in 1951, and *The Burnt Offering* appeared in 1956. His third short "novel of expiation," *The Boychik*, appears for the first time in English in this volume.[1] The other works by Goes that are included are tributes to Buber, accounts of Goes's conversations with him, interpretations of Buber's thought, and extensions of his ideas in specific incidents of human encounter. They are the work of a writer who is neither a philosopher nor a systematic theologian but, rather, a pastor and poet in the tradition of Eduard Mörike and Jeremias Gotthelf. His novels, essays, and sermons are in the spirit of what Buber called "philosophical anthropology."

Martin Buber was born in Vienna on February 8, 1878, and died in Jerusalem on June 13, 1965. His early life was spent in Lvov (Lemberg), then a part of Poland, and Buber called himself a Polish Jew. His intellectual heritage, however, was thoroughly German. From 1923 to 1933 he was a professor at the University of Frankfurt. In 1933 he withdrew from German public life to become the spiritual leader of centers for Jewish adult education until his departure for Palestine in 1938. He then became Professor of Social Philosophy at the Hebrew University in Jerusalem.

Albrecht Goes was born on March 22, 1908, at Langenbeutigen, a small town in Württemberg. His homeland is Swabia, the birthplace of such German intellectual figures of international renown as Friedrich Schiller, Friedrich Hölderlin, G. F. Hegel, David Friedrich Strauss, and Hermann Hesse, not to mention such honored poets as Mörike, Uhland, Kerner, Schwab, and Hauff. Goes was drafted into the German army as an enlisted man in 1940 and was stationed on the Eastern front in Poland and Hungary, later becoming a chaplain. It was during these years that he experienced the

---

[1] The title of the German original is *Das Löffelchen* (1965). The author's alternate title, "Das Jüngelchen," justifies the title chosen for this translation.

encounters described in his essay "Encounter in Hungary" and the novels *Unquiet Night* and *The Boychik*. Although he no longer holds a pastoral office, he still preaches twice a month in Stuttgart churches and enjoys a distinguished reputation as a prolific essayist, poet, novelist, literary critic, and interpreter of Mozart, Bach, Goethe, and Mörike.

Martin Buber and Albrecht Goes occupied the same platform at a very controversial event in Buber's life—his acceptance of the Peace Prize of the German Book Trade in 1953. At Buber's suggestion, Albrecht Goes had been invited to be the main speaker on that occasion ("Martin Buber, Our Support"). This public meeting is the high point in the dialogue between a representative of the German people and a "surviving arch-Jew," as Buber described himself at that event. Buber and Goes first met at Heidelberg a few weeks prior to the Peace Prize ceremony in the historic St. Paul's Church in Frankfurt. The first document of their dialogue, however, is dated August 4, 1934—a letter from the young pastor Albrecht Goes to Martin Buber in Heppenheim on the Bergstrasse, a Hessian town near Darmstadt. Nineteen years later this letter was the point of departure from which Buber resumed their dialogue. In a letter dated Jerusalem, June 6, 1953, Buber writes that he has reread the letter of 1934 with undiminished emotion and that he is "more its recipient today than I was then."

Albrecht Goes became aware of the question of anti-Semitism in Germany at the early age of fourteen. The Jewish Foreign Minister of Germany, Walther Rathenau, was assassinated in 1922; young Goes was deeply moved and wept bitterly over the event. He describes his resolution at that time in the essay "Nothing but to Live":

I want to see what goes on. I want to see the other fellow the way he is. Perhaps he is quite alien to me; perhaps he is not a pleasant sort. But no idea—and all ideas have something inimical to life about them—shall prevent me from recognizing what is alive across all distances.

Thus began his early concern for the Jews, a concern which has had an important reciprocal effect on his interest in Martin Buber.

Goes's early works, both prose and poetry, reflect a harmonious, secure life—the everyday events of his family, childhood, and later the routine lives of his parishioners. The rise of the Nazis to power apparently took the sheltered village pastor by surprise. It shattered the security of his life and caused him to turn to Martin Buber as a source of spiritual support. In the letter of 1934 he wrote Buber about incidents in his pastoral duties and of the importance of Buber's works to him. Goes had read Buber's classic works *Ich und Du* [*I and Thou*] and *Zwiesprache* [*Dialogue*] in the course of his theological studies at Berlin and Tübingen. The letter is couched in a vague, indirect language necessary in the Germany of 1934. He says that Buber's words on responsibility from his essay "My Way to Hasidism" (included in this volume on pages 3–4) were as close to him as *Genesis* or *I Corinthians 13*. He asks Buber what form his own responsibility should take:

But now it happens . . . that these circles [of responsibility] collide with walls, with shores which do not suffer it and its responsible participation in the things of a strange world, and which brutally and decisively reject this responsibility, their own and mine. Tell me, sir, what attitude is the man of responsibility commanded to take in the world . . . I mean, in the world that seems to be built upon a different basic premise, which speaks a different language, which is simply different? . . . As a very young man who simply can no longer get his bearings in the otherness of these times, I ask you whether you, a wise man, can tell me whether I should want to be a doctor to treat what is incurable.

He then cites several specific types of people whom he has recently encountered in his pastoral ministry, and adds:

And these are only the concrete cases of recent weeks, and behind these are virtually unfathomable connections and bundles of a strange humanity. I do not complain; I only ask.

Buber replied to Goes in 1934 and referred the young pastor to his essay of 1919 "What Is To Be Done" (included in this volume on pages 5–8) and specifically to the admonition "Thou shalt not withhold thyself." Goes interpreted Buber's words as an exhortation to deal with the problems of everyday life without withholding his counsel from the people whom he encountered.

One question cannot be avoided here: Why did all the "good" Germans like Albrecht Goes not actively oppose the Nazi regime and lay their lives on the line as did another Protestant pastor, Dietrich Bonhoeffer? The answer to this question lies not in philosophical argumentation and attempts at justification but in a realistic recognition of human strength and weakness. Buber's own answer was given in his address at the above-mentioned Frankfurt ceremony when he said:

When I think of the German people of the days of Auschwitz and Treblinka, I behold, first of all, the great many who knew that the monstrous event was taking place and did not oppose it. But my heart, which is acquainted with the weakness of men, refuses to condemn my neighbour for not prevailing upon himself to become a martyr.

Martin Buber preferred imperfect people to the perfection of intellect. In his essay "Books and People" he admits that he encounters "entirely pleasant books far more frequently than entirely pleasant people." His words here are an extension of his premise that "all real living is meeting" or "encounter." Albrecht Goes, too, characterizes himself as a man who is "often moved by great events, but challenged only by encounter"; his only inspiration comes from the "drama of encounter —encounter of the multifariousness of life." The essay "Encounter in Hungary" (included here on pages 30–34), written about the same time as Buber's more theoretical treatment of meeting, or encounter, relates how such a meeting took place under very difficult circumstances between the chaplain and two Jewish doctors. It shows how one can often transform fear and distrust into hope and fulfillment through genuine dialogue.

The postwar works of Albrecht Goes included here can be seen as an attempt to show the meaning of what he once called a "minor martyrdom"—a martyrdom which makes daily sacrifices to alleviate suffering, to soften brutality where it crosses one's path, and to save what can be saved. But they also reveal something of Goes's experience with the "healing venom of self-doubt." He appears to see himself as a self-appointed expiator of Germany's guilt—not so much of its collective guilt as the real, existential guilt that every individual shares in all human guilt. Buber carefully distinguished between neurotic feelings of guilt and real guilt when he told American psychiatrists at the Washington School of Psychiatry in 1957:

I have seen three important and, to me, dear men fall into long illnesses from their failing to stand the test in the days of an acute community guilt. The share of the psychogenic element in the illness could hardly be estimated, but its action was unmistakable. One of them refused to acknowledge his self-contradiction before the court of his spirit. The second resisted recognizing as serious a slight error he remembered that was attached to a very serious chain of circumstances. The third, however, would not let himself be forgiven by God for the blunder of a moment because he did not forgive himself.[2]

Buber's concern with matters of guilt and guilt feelings may have been an outcome of his dialogue with men like Albrecht Goes. Several of Goes's works, particularly *Unquiet Night* and *The Boychik*, show a profound awareness of Buber's careful distinction between real and imagined guilt and the necessity of recognizing even minor passive acts that contribute to "a very serious chain of circumstances."

[2] *The Knowledge of Man*, edited with an Introductory Essay (Chap. I) by Maurice Friedman, translated by Maurice Friedman and Ronald Gregor Smith (New York: Harper Torchbooks, 1966), "Guilt and Guilt Feelings," translated by Maurice Friedman, p. 126; quoted by permission of Harper & Row, Publishers.

Albrecht Goes's reputation was established in Germany by his short novel *Unquiet Night,* which appeared in 1950. It was followed by translations into fourteen languages and television and movie versions in Germany. Although the work was written before Buber and Goes met personally, it reveals a deep understanding and application of Buber's premise that "all real living is meeting." The chaplain's task on that night of unrest is a direct personal encounter with the deserter Baranowski. His responsibility to administer the symbols of Christian salvation is not shirked, but this responsibility can be discharged only through the medium of a man-to-man encounter. In this highly potentialized life situation, no other life is real for the chaplain except his meeting with Baranowski. The Christian message of eternal life will come from a man and will be administered to a man. Their dialogue is thus a dialogue of sacramental import.

Unquiet Night is autobiographical down to much of its detail. Goes's next novel, *The Burnt Offering,* is based only indirectly on events which Goes heard about much later. It deals specifically with the question of the persecution of the Jews and gives an example of how some Germans did what they could to alleviate the suffering of the Jews. The theme of sacrifice plunges down from its mythical and Biblical pedestal into the raw here-and-now of Nazi Germany. Following the Old Testament analogy of God's rejection of Abraham's sacrifice, Frau Walker's "major martyrdom" is rejected in favor of a "minor martyrdom" of continued daily sacrifice in service to those about her. On October 19, 1954, Martin Buber wrote to Albrecht Goes concerning *The Burnt Offering:*

Your story moved us deeply. It is a document of genuine, heavy-hearted humanity which knows about sacrifice and will surely have the effect you have in mind.

The third novel of expiation, *The Boychik,* bears the dedication "Martin Buber dem Lehrer, dem Vater, dem Freund" ["To Martin Buber—teacher, father, friend"]. Buber gave his

approval to the carefully worded dedication and saw an advance copy of the book a few months prior to his death. The
novel returns to events from Goes's war experiences. In his
essay "Go, Suffer, Wait" (included here on pages 258–275)
Goes wrote:

And we know that the picture would not be a fair one if we did not
speak of the Jewish peasant—I met one in Roumania—of the well-
versed craftsman that our army hospitals in Eastern Europe employed because he was important to them, only to be killed by the
men of the Security Service whenever they pleased—and they did
please.

The craftsman of whom he spoke here was called Stefan in
The Boychik. The story appears to be an illustration of the
second man in Buber's three examples to American psychiatrists—the man who "resisted recognizing as serious a slight
error he remembered that was attached to a very serious chain
of circumstances." But here Goes depicts a man now in the act
of recognizing his existential error, no matter how slight.

None of the personnel at the military hospital took any active part in Stefan's execution. But several of them, including
the chaplain himself, committed little indiscretions which,
when added together, resulted in Stefan's and Leib's death.
They took Stefan into their compound because they needed
him and gave him the name Stefan to protect him, as they
thought, from being identified as a Jew. Their "protection"
led to his and Leib's death. On another level Stefan's fate is a
symbol of the exploitation of the Jews by the Germans. When
he has served his function and the clinic is to be evacuated, he
must be eliminated. It is a microcosmic image of what Buber
discusses in his essay. "The End of the German-Jewish Symbiosis."

Goes's expressions of Buber's teachings in "fictional" form
are in keeping with Buber's own interpretation of Hasidism
through the tales of Hasidic rabbis. Buber once wrote that
"what Hasidism here expresses mythically is a central knowl-

edge that is communicable only in images, not in concepts." [3] Thus all three of Goes's novels illustrate the efficacy of genuine dialogue in human encounter and reflect authentic images of man very close to Buber's thought. The author's attitude toward guilt in the three works undergoes a development from an approach to guilt as an inevitable consequence of being human in *Unquiet Night,* a symbolic expiation of collective guilt in *The Burnt Offering,* and, finally, a healthy acknowledgment of existential guilt in *The Boychik.*

The fictional works in *Men of Dialogue* are followed by two addresses and two short narratives based on Goes's personal encounters with Martin Buber. Although Goes provides no systematic introduction to Buber's philosophy, his insights into Buber the man furnish access to Buber's thought from a viewpoint frequently missed by more objective scholars. Buber held that no person, thing, or experience can have any significant meaning to the observer unless that observer recognizes the responsibility of response. The observer cannot realize his own potential as "I" until he enters into relationship with his "Thou." He showed disdain for anything that "smacks of an unbinding [*unverbindliche*] *Weltanschauung.*" [4] The personal tone of response in Goes's "A Living Legend" and "The 'Patriarch' from Jerusalem" therefore needs no defense. Although the two addresses show that Goes had acquired a scholarly knowledge of Buber's thought, they also reveal a response to that thought which goes far beyond scholarship.

Buber read the manuscript of "The 'Patriarch' from Jerusalem" and wrote to Albrecht Goes from Jerusalem on December 19, 1962:

With a very special joy I have read your radio address which was recently sent to me. It has such a beautiful authenticity because a story is really told in it.

[3] *Hasidism and Modern Man,* edited and translated by Maurice Friedman (New York: Harper Torchbooks, 1966), p. 33.

[4] *The Philosophy of Martin Buber,* Vol. XII of *The Library of Living Philosophers,* edited by Paul Schilpp and Maurice Friedman (La Salle, Illinois: Open Court, 1967), p. 714.

The remaining selections in this volume show the similarity of thought and intellectual propinquity between Martin Buber the Jew and Albrecht Goes the German Christian. Buber's "Second Response" and Goes's "A Morning Hour at Worms" are two reflections on the meaning of the cathedral and the Jewish cemetery at Worms. Buber reaffirms his belief in Israel's mission in the world—a mission not to be abrogated because of the advent of Christianity. Goes expresses his joy that both the cathedral and the cemetery, two archetypal phenomena, are still standing after the holocaust of the Second World War.

Buber's essay "The Children" reveals his deep concern for the spiritual welfare of the Jews in the Germany of 1933. As a practical and spiritual Zionist he advocates that parents teach their children Jewish substance and form their lives in a Jewish way. Goes's essay of 1959, "Nothing but to Live," depicts a mother and her child after the years of deprivation and horror are over. His words here show how fully the German Protestant pastor feels himself identified with the sufferings and hopes of the people of Israel.

The three remaining contributions by Martin Buber are not altogether comfortable reading for Jews, Germans, or Americans. They must be understood in the context of the time and situation and in the light of Buber's independent position as a spiritual Zionist. Buber was one of the founders of *Ichud* [Unity], an organization favoring a binational Jewish-Arabic state of Israel. Buber's struggle for Arab-Jewish reconciliation is a part of his thought which is little known in the English-speaking world and not appreciated in Israel. Schalom Ben-Chorin writes: "It was Buber's tragedy that he had no response here from the Arabic side and also met with little understanding in his own camp." [5] Buber's vision of a state of Israel with

[5] *Zwiesprache mit Martin Buber* (Munich: List Verlag, 1966), p. 101. Ben-Chorin's statement appears to apply only to affairs after the War of 1948 since there was some important Arab response to *Ichud*, and there were Arab members in *Ichud* prior to 1948.

an Arab and a Jewish sector was totally rejected by the majority of the Israeli population. His decision to accept the Goethe
Prize of the City of Hamburg in 1953 and the Peace Prize of
the German Book Trade that same year unleashed a torrent of
criticism and left him isolated in Israel.

"The End of the German-Jewish Symbiosis" and "They and
We" were written in 1939, shortly after Buber's arrival in Palestine and before the coming systematic annihilation of the
Jews was in full progress. Buber's declaration of a decisive and
permanent end of the German-Jewish symbiosis resounds with
bold prophetic authority: "The symbiosis itself is terminated
and cannot return." But his announcement of termination is
tempered with an undercurrent of profound sadness and careful distinction between the German state and the German
people—a distinction which Buber repeated at the Peace Prize
ceremony in Frankfurt in 1953 even after the full extent of the
holocaust was known. Although the preponderance of guilt is
laid firmly upon the leaders of the Nazi regime, Buber spares
neither his own people nor Germany's enemies in outlining the
historical motivations for the persecution.

Buber labels the systematic, organized nature of anti-Semitism as treason of the German state against its people. But in
Palestine the Jews' struggle against Hitler must take the form
of hard work in setting up "the Kingdom of the God of Justice" in this land. In "Silence and Outcry" Buber is distressed
by the infusion of political matters into attempts to rescue the
Jews. His solution to the emergencies of the time is what he
calls "this cruelly sober one: to save as many Jews as is at all
possible; to bring them here or take them to other places; to
save them by fully realistic treatment of the various practical
questions with all manner of means at our disposal. . . ."

The addresses and essays by Albrecht Goes which follow are
typical of the pastor-poet's efforts since the war to keep alive
the memory of what has happened. He is aware that such
crimes cannot really be atoned for, but knowledge and awareness can make men vigilant and determined that such heinous

deeds will not be repeated. He sees a continuing tide of anti-Semitism in Germany—a rampant plague whose ravenous appetite has not been assuaged by millions of murders. In the address "Go, Suffer, Wait" he says that "we all know that anti-Semitism is not a *Weltanschauung* or a way of life but a plague; one has to be against it the way one is against the plague—unequivocally and without any ifs, ands, or buts." The positive means by which anti-Semitism is to be overcome in Germany is knowledge. This conviction led Goes to Martin Buber's thought as a rich source of knowledge of the Hebrew heritage. In his preaching, speaking, and writing he seeks to keep alive the knowledge of Jewish culture in Germany. His latest collection of sermons[6] is permeated with quotations from Buber's Old Testament translations, references to the Jewish-German cultural heritage and to Dachau and Auschwitz. He will not let Germany forget. His insistence on keeping the memory alive is not, however, a masochistic wallowing in the mire of the *unbewältigte Vergangenheit,* a past guilt still unatoned for. He recognizes that "the evocation of phantoms is a bleak undertaking." Instead of such an evocation, one should take an attitude of serious joy in the task of a daily rededication to working together for reconciliation.

Martin Buber and Albrecht Goes were not intimate friends. Their dialogue in person comprised only three or four lengthy conversations; their correspondence, consisting of about sixteen letters over a period of some thirty years, reveals a reserve characteristic of both men. The selections in this book show that such a dialogue is not measured in hours spent together or in number of letters exchanged. Their dialogue is important because of its representative significance for Protestant and Jew, Germany and Israel, scholar and poet. They never met as representatives—such a meeting would have been totally foreign to their own beliefs about human personality—but their dialogue symbolizes a new possibility of human encounter.

[6] *Der Knecht macht keinen Lärm* (Hamburg: Friedrich Wittig Verlag, 1968).

People can come into vital relationship with people in spite of all artificial and real barriers: The chaplain can reach Baranowski in his cell, Frau Walker can fight hate with sacrificial love, the memory of Stefan and Leib can be kept alive, the Jew can meet the German Christian, and the cab driver can meet the philosopher. The I can meet its Thou.

E. WILLIAM ROLLINS
North Carolina State University
February, 1969

HARRY ZOHN
Brandeis University
February, 1969

MEN OF DIALOGUE: Martin Buber and Albrecht Goes

Martin Buber ✡ ON RESPONSIBILITY

from "My Way to Hasidism"

EACH MAN HAS AN INFINITE SPHERE OF RESPONSIBILITY, RE-
sponsibility before the infinite. He moves, he talks, he looks,
and each of his movements, each of his words, each of his
glances causes waves to surge in the happening of the world: he
cannot know how strong and how far-reaching. Each man with
all his being and doing determines the fate of the world in a
measure unknowable to him and all others; for the causality
which we can perceive is indeed only a tiny segment of the
inconceivable, manifold, invisible working of all upon all.
Thus every human action is a vessel of infinite responsibility.

But there are men who are hourly accosted by infinite responsibility in a special, specially active form. I do not mean
the rulers and statesmen who have to determine the external
destiny of great communities; their sphere of action is all-
embracing but, in order to be effective, they turn away from
the individual, enormously threatened lives that glance at
them with thousandfold question, to the general that appears
to them unseeing. I mean those who withstand the thousand-
fold-questioning glance of individual lives, who give true answer to the trembling mouth of the needy creature who time

after time demands from them decision; I mean the zaddikim,[1] I mean the true zaddik. That is the man who hourly measures the depths of responsibility with the sounding lead of his words. He speaks—and knows that his speech is destiny. He does not decide the fate of countries and peoples, but ever again only the small and great course of an individual life, so finite and yet so boundless. Men come to him, and each desires his opinion, his help. And even though it is corporal and semi-corporal needs that they bring to him, in his world-insight there is nothing corporal that cannot be transfigured, nothing material that cannot be raised to spirit. And it is this that he does for all: *he elevates their need before he satisfies it.*

Thus he is the helper in spirit, the teacher of world-meaning, the conveyor to the divine sparks. The world needs him, the perfected man; it awaits him, it awaits him ever again.

[1] Saintly persons.—Eds.

Martin Buber ❦ WHAT IS TO BE DONE?

IF YOU MEAN BY THIS QUESTION, "WHAT IS ONE TO DO?"—THERE is no answer. *One* is not to do anything. *One* cannot help himself, with *one* there is nothing to begin, with *one* it is all over. He who contents himself with explaining or discussing or asking what *one* is to do talks and lives in a vacuum.

But he who poses the question with the earnestness of his soul on his lips and means, "What have I to do?"—he is taken by the hand by comrades he does not know but whom he will soon become familiar with, and they answer (he listens to their wonderful reply and marvels when only this follows):

"You shall not withhold yourself."

The old eternal answer! But its truth is once again new and intact.

The questioner regards the truth and his astonishment becomes fruitful. He nods. And as soon as he nods, he feels on the palms of his hands the blood-warmth of togetherness. It speaks for him, but it seems to him as if he himself spoke:

"You shall not withhold yourself.

"You, imprisoned in the shells in which society, state, church, school, economy, public opinion, and your own pride have stuck you, indirect one among indirect ones, break through your shells, become direct; man, have contact with men!

5

"Ancient rot and mold is between man and man. Forms born of meaning degenerate into convention, respect into mistrust, modesty in communicating into stingy taciturnity. Now and then men grope toward one another in anxious delirium —and miss one another, for the heap of rot is between them. Clear it away, you and you and you! Establish directness, formed out of meaning, respectful, modest directness between men!

"You shall not withhold yourself.

"Solitary one, two solitudes are interwoven in your life. Only one shall you root out: shutting oneself up, withdrawing into oneself, standing apart—the solitude of the men incapable of community. The other you shall now really establish and consolidate—the necessary ever-again-becoming-solitary of the strong. In order to gather new strength, the strong man must from time to time call home his forces into a solitude where he rests in the community of the things that have been and those that will come, and is nourished by them, so that he may go forth with new strength to the community of those who now exist.

"To it you shall learn to go forth—go forth and not withhold yourself.

"You shall help. Each man you meet needs help, each needs *your* help. That is the thousandfold happening of each moment, that the need of help and the capacity to help make way for one another so that each not only does not know about the other but does not even know about himself. It is the nature of man to leave equally unnoticed the innermost need and the innermost gift of his own soul, although at times, too, a deep hour reminds him of them. You shall awaken in the other the need of help, in yourself the capacity to help. Even when you yourself are in need—and you are—you can help others and, in so doing, help yourself.

"He who calls forth the helping word in himself, experiences the word. He who offers support strengthens the support in himself. He who bestows comfort deepens the comfort in himself. He who effects salvation, to him salvation is disclosed."

The voices of the unknown, the familiar become silent. The questioner reflects on what has been said. But soon they begin again, transformed, beyond him.

"And you:

"You who are shut in in the fortress of your spirit, who admit no one who does not know the password, enthroned in withholding, and you who exchange the sign of recognition with the fellow-conspirators of the secret alliance, you who walk in withholding, the time has come when you must forget word and sign—or be submerged! For not otherwise will you find the new word and sign that will bind the coming torrent.

"The torrent that with facile words you call the crowd.

"Who has made the crowd so great? He who hates it and he who despises it, he who is horrified by it, he who is disgusted by it, each indeed who says, the crowd!—all of them have made it so great that it now wants to surge up to your spiritual fortresses and your secret alliances.

"But now is the time, and now is still the time for the work of conquering.

"Make the crowd no longer a crowd!

"Out of forlorn and impotent men, out of men who have attacked one another through forlornness and impotence, the shapeless thing has come into being—deliver man from it, shape the shapeless to community! Break the withholding, throw yourselves into the surging waves, reach for and grasp hands, lift, help, lead, authenticate spirit and alliance in the trial of the abyss, make the crowd no longer a crowd!

"Some say civilization must be preserved through 'subduing.' There is no civilization to preserve. And there is no longer a subduing! But what may ascend out of the flood will be decided by whether you throw yourselves into it as seeds of true community.

"No longer through exclusion but only inclusion can the kingdom be established. When it no longer horrifies you and no longer disgusts you, when you redeem the crowd into men and strike even the heart of the crude, the greedy, the stingy with your love, then and then alone is there present, in the midst of the end, the new beginning.

"You hesitate, you doubt—you know from history that each unchaining is answered by new chaining? You do not yet understand, then, that history no longer holds. But the day is not far off when the well-informed security will be pulverized in the souls. Recognize this before it is too late!"

Again the voices become silent. But now they do not begin again. Silently the world waits for the spirit.

PEACE PRIZE OF THE GERMAN
BOOK TRADE [1953]

PEACE PRIZE OF THE GERMAN BOOK TRADE, 1953.

THE CITATION

TO

MARTIN BUBER

Man of Truth, who proclaims and fashions a humane
spirit
Suffusing all living things;
Interpreter of his people's destiny in history,
Philosopher of Dialogue,
Theologian and Educator,

The Financial Exchange of German Publishers and Book
Dealers,
in respectful appreciation of his life and work,
awards the PEACE PRIZE OF THE GERMAN BOOK
TRADE.

Frankfurt-am-Main, St. Paul's Church,
September, 1953.

(Signed)
DR. ARTHUR GEORGI,
Chairman

Albrecht Goes ✿ MARTIN BUBER, OUR SUPPORT

ONE ANSWERS A LETTER IN THE QUIET OF ONE'S STUDY AND NOT, as you might say, before a solemn public assembly. And yet this sort of thing is just what I intend to do here. For even though it certainly seems inadmissible to us to speak of the emotions which may be crowding in upon you, Martin Buber, upon your return after so many years (and what years!) to the city of your former activity—the emotions are your own and our words cannot reach them—still, it seems right for us not to hold our feelings back. For us this is truly the hour of a wish fulfilled. Anyone who has waited for twenty years to be allowed to express quite directly for once greetings and thanks to Martin Buber may well be impatient. Nor should he be disturbed by the idea that he may be speaking too privately. He does not speak privately. He speaks for those who were not denied a support at an anxious and difficult moment in their lives when the important thing was to have a support, and you were this support.

That was in 1933, 1934, and the years after that. Before our eyes tyranny occupied one position after another; the individual was beset by the dilemma of speaking untruthfully and keeping silent untruthfully—assailed doubly and more if by virtue of his position he bore a daily responsibility for others. But at that time, when much of life that we had relied upon

12

was vanishing and many helpers were becoming helpless, there was this certainty: by his lamp at Heppenheim on the Bergstrasse sits Martin Buber, and we can put our slips of paper outside his door, as the Hasidim put their slips in front of the doors of the Maggid or of Rabbi Shmelke of Nikolsburg. This is what counted. What could be written on those slips of paper? Well, whoever sat down to write to Heppenheim probably asked simply: What are we to do? Then, as now, the answer must read as it read as early as 1919 in an admonition of Martin Buber: "You shall not withhold yourself." And then as now it points in no other direction but to that which is, at any time, the closest, that to which we at all times, in evil days as well, owe the memory of Truth and Reality.

Such an answer, once it is given, could suffice for all time. But could not the beautiful miracle happen that it be given once again in another hour of the world and of life? You, Martin Buber, had given an immediate answer to the man who had written you nineteen years ago. But recently, even before I knew that I would have the distinction of being permitted to speak here today—it happened that you answered me another time. This second letter did not come from Heppenheim, but was postmarked Jerusalem. It was a letter such as one does not receive every year; and if that first time I wrote I did not write for myself alone, I am even less the sole recipient of the answer today. In fact, everything I have to say at this festive moment is bound up intimately with this letter of yours. Here it is:

Before this trip to Europe I felt it to be my duty once more to look through my correspondence from 1933 to 1953 as far as it has been preserved, and as I did so, your letter of August 4, 1934, in which you ask about the attitude of the responsible individual, affected me in a special way. I felt the questioning heart of the then young—you wrote "very young"—man more strongly than I did at that time. The way the world is constituted today one must not keep silent about any experience of a genuine closeness; that is why I am writing to you. I do not know to what extent you are still identical with the writer of that letter (I am today more its recipient than I was then), but certainly you still have a sufficiently intimate relationship to him to convey to him my greetings in all directness.

I did convey those greetings. I also saw that cloud whose darkness you perceived for a moment, the cloud of fear that a man might have forgotten and abjured in nineteen years. I have seen it, as we always see when Platen's verses move over our hearts:

> And the man that I was and long ago
> Exchanged for another self, where is he now?

But this is only a cloud, and I assume you wrote your letter because you believe the addressee capable of being the real recipient—he, too, more so than he was nineteen years ago—who is in need of the greeting of genuine clos ness, in need of a support.

A support. . . . Let me demonstrate with a few sentences by way of defining and interpreting what is meant by this appellation: Martin Buber, our support.

Whom did we mean then, whom do we mean now? Whom did we not mean, who do we not mean? We did not and do not mean the dictator. That first letter was written out of consternation at the evil spectacle of someone presuming to give himself the title *Führer*—and this word was supposed to mean the leader of a land in which the *Urworte, Orphisch,*[1] the Isenheim Altar, and the B-Minor Mass had come into being. We did and do mean this: A man who was susceptible to experiences could by this one experience be made immune to being misled by "leaders." The truth which is directed at me and to which I owe an answer does not come from a *Führer's* command to me, no matter what kind it may be. He who lives by fiat does not live as a personality. A bondsman does not listen. But who will help him, the unformed man, when help is needed? Not the commanding spirit, but the questioning one. Not Pope John XXII, but Meister Eckhart; Blaise Pascal, not the ecclesiastical court; not Bishop Mynster and his unshakable

---

[1] A poetic work by Goethe (1817).—Eds.

assurance, but, rather, his opponent, Søren Kierkegaard; and, similarly, the voice of the frightened, the uncompromising, be it the soft voice of Father Zosima or the passionate voice of Simone Weil.

Not the dictator is meant, nor the preceptor. How have you become the person that you are? Where did you study? What school do you come from? A fool's speech in Shakespeare—so you might answer—has taught me; a string passage in the Mozart Quintet which we heard today is a pure message; the lines of a Rembrandt drawing reveal secrets enough; and so do the gestures with which my host served the vegetables at the table, a beckoning, tears in the night, a smile at parting. But it is never the idolatry of words, not the student's looseleaf notebook, nor the system which is unchangeable.

Resisting the dictator and alien to the preceptor, a guest at many tables and yet traveling onward, toward something where many things would become an entity in which connections would become plausible—this is how we found our way to you, this is how we encountered your words:

I, myself, have no doctrine. He who expects of me a teaching . . . will always be disillusioned. And it would seem to me, indeed, that in this hour of history the crucial thing is not to possess a fixed doctrine, but rather to recognize eternal reality and out of its depth to be able to face the reality of the present. No way can be pointed to in this desert night. One's purpose must be to help men of today to stand fast, with their souls in readiness, until the dawn breaks and a path becomes visible where none suspected it.*

And now you opened up to us the Tales of the Hasidim, and we saw the Baal-Shem, the Great Maggid, and all his sons and grandsons in body and spirit. We were companions of the nameless Hasidim who lived in the simple, great certainty that it is possible to "see God in everything and reach Him through every pure deed." We were not instructed but shown a direction; life-masters, not school-masters, spoke with us; not finished things came into our hands but the fullness of possibili-

* See Note 11, p. 192.

ties, and the reflection of the primal light was over them. And when we now asked our questions—not in Berdichev, but here and now—when we brought our questions to you, your countenance, the countenance of the answerer, appeared to us like the countenance of many eras. The answer was given in the language of our time, perhaps in the form of a discussion of the most recent existentialist philosophy, but he who was really perceptive saw the patriarch from Rymanov, saw the Zaddik—majestic, but at the same time close as a brother; fiery, but at the same time smiling; artful, but also full of simplicity; one minute joking with the drayman, the next moment joyously dancing, then again composed to pronounce the blessing the way it is pronounced on the great Day of Atonement.

As for the questions—wherever men do not remain on the outskirts, they are everywhere the same: How can fruitful life unfold when there is evil, when we are harnessed together with the abysses, the negations, and when these possess their strongest bastion within ourselves? And, with the images of God crumbling before our eyes, how can we remain certain of the existence of God? And, how can the profound loneliness of our human existence be overcome in truth?

When these questions faced us in ever new guises, you were far away from us. You had been driven from the country to which you had given the strength of your work and whose language you had spoken and written with the severe grace of a Hofmannsthal. But you were not beyond our reach. For, every time after the end of the deluge that we received news from Israel, with passionate concern—it cannot be expressed otherwise—and read about the Kibbutzim, the cooperatives which were now winning the soil of Eretz Israel with ineffable patience, with fiery impatience, probably with impetuous passion as well—on all such occasions the image of you became part of these images. We saw you, Martin Buber, sheltered in one of the big buildings of the Hebrew University, a teacher, a professor, to be sure, but at bottom committed to the same cause that these settlers were serving.

He who tends the soil, what does he tend? He is concerned with the soil of the fields, the depth of the earth, the subterranean, the moisture or dryness of the root beds, the resistances, the underground parasites. And the sky is his concern, the heights, the active light, the salubrious rain. And he is concerned with those who help with the seeding and the harvesting, with their lives, their working strength, their joy, their community.

And thus we saw you, too, committed to the soil of Israel—more, to the soil of mankind—in a threefold pledge . . . to its depth, its darkness, the impenetrable, the unknown. You ask about the dark sides of life, about evil? Take care, says the answer, that it be not repressed, not choked off, least of all psychoanalytically sublimated. Take care, rather, that it be recognized as a spark of that glory with which the "cups of the deep" are filled. Take care that the "evil inclination" be included in the love of God; be aware of it as the burning bush that wants to be seized by the divine fire. Your darkness does not want indulgence, but it does need preparation, attention, direction, and, more than that, love.

And committed to the soil and to the arch of the sky over this soil, which is over its plants and grasses with life-giving sun and fresh morning dew, thus meaning God and now—we invoke Pascal's *mémorial*—"the God of Abraham, Isaac, and Jacob, not the God of the philosophers and scholars." It will be necessary to abandon images and to remain mindful that God's *word* is voice, not God's letter. But it is at the same time needful to examine whether wherever "God" is said there does not really prevail an eclipse of God, because no vis-à-vis is being addressed, because no "And God said" is being answered in truth. Thus two things are achieved: The icons are taken off the walls of those too easily assured, the images which prevent them from recognizing Him who is above all images; and the glass roof which someone may allow to serve as a substitute for heaven is inexorably called a glass roof.

But there is a third thing: Committed to the soil, and asking about the center even more than about the depth and the height, Martin Buber's basic concern is with man, not with God, for the Eternal does not need our worry about His realization in this world. It is the concern over all human togetherness, the concern over whether those who have to do with one another "really have to do with one another" or whether they speak in all eternity only their bitter monologues, either knowing them to be monologues or imagining that talking past another is a dialogue. "The really fateful question for mankind," said Buber in his farewell message to his American audience, "is whether there is direct, unreserved dialogue, genuine conversation between men of different kind and mentality."

Concern. . . . Concern over the I and its Thou. Over the togetherness and simultaneousness of religious service and human service. Over bringing together what is falling apart. And this in such a way that always the smallest sphere is kept before our eyes; the area of the dialogue, with the presentiment and the knowledge, like a breath blowing in through the window, of the great sphere: the people, the nations, all of mankind.

Concern. . . . But concern is trust. The trust which Martin Buber radiates is the trust of the true Zaddik. It is the trust in the full power of that joy which once moved Rabbi Yehudi to send out minstrels to aid his moribund teacher with the power of melody. It is the trust in the efficacy of that serene love which made Rabbi Wolf ask his unmannerly guest to give him slices of radish, so as not to shame him. It is that trust which does not withhold itself, which, to put it once more in Hasidic form, wants to be brick rather than sheet iron. Sheet iron does serve as a roof for a house, but a better thing happens if the heart of the man who watches over the community is like a brick, "shaken by all their sorrows, so that it threatens to break at any moment, and yet enduring." And this trust includes the readiness to be sad with others and to keep silent for a long time, because we are united by the insight that it is hard really to love one's fellow men, because, in the words of the Sasov

Rabbi, frequently enough we do not know what ails the other fellow.

To be sure, the melancholia which could prevail here is from the very beginning recognized as the great temptation from the depths. Amid oppressiveness there early resounded the watchman's call of the Baal-Shem (you have told about it more than once): "Arise from sleep with fervor." And the image of Henoch the patriarch achieved actuality, of the cobbler who with each stitch of his awl joined together God and the Shekhinah, that is to say, the Eternal and that majesty of God which was let down into the world, dragged in the dust, banished into exile, but which wants to be sought and found as glory in that very place.

But such service forever committed your life to one thing: love of mankind. And it forever excluded from it one thing: the spirit of negation.

By virtue of such service you have become a support for us. Not the dictator who wants to coerce, nor the preceptor whose share is the parts, but one who accompanies us through the endless duration of the moment, who opens our eyes to the immeasurable grace of the moment.

According to an old saying, the continued existence of the world rests on thirty-six righteous men. Since you, Martin Buber, are here among us, we are tempted to add another sentence. But we should interfere with the careful hesitation, the sacred *ritardando* of your law of life, if we were to utter it.

Martin Buber ✌ GENUINE DIALOGUE
AND THE POSSIBILITIES OF PEACE

I CANNOT EXPRESS MY THANKS TO THE GERMAN BOOK TRADE FOR the honor conferred on me without at the same time setting forth the sense in which I have accepted it, just as I earlier accepted the Hanseatic Goethe Prize given me by the University of Hamburg.

About a decade ago a considerable number of Germans—there must have been many thousands of them—under the indirect command of the German government and the direct command of its representatives, killed millions of my people in a systematically prepared and executed procedure whose organized cruelty cannot be compared with any previous historical event. I, who am one of those who remained alive, have only in a formal sense a common humanity with those who took part in this action. They have so radically removed themselves from the human sphere, so transposed themselves into a sphere of monstrous inhumanity inaccessible to my conception, that not even hatred, much less an overcoming of hatred, was able to arise in me. And what am I that I could here presume to "forgive"!

With the German people it is otherwise. From my youth on I have taken the real existence of peoples most seriously. But I have never, in the face of any historical moment, past or present, allowed the concrete multiplicity existing at that moment within a people—the concrete inner dialectic, rising to contra-diction—to be obscured by the levelling concept of a totality constituted and acting in just such a way and no other.

When I think of the German people of the days of Auschwitz and Treblinka, I behold, first of all, the great many who knew that the monstrous event was taking place and did not oppose it. But my heart, which is acquainted with the weakness of men, refuses to condemn my neighbor for not prevailing upon himself to become a martyr. Next there emerges before me the mass of those who remained ignorant of what was withheld from the German public, and who did not try to discover what reality lay behind the rumors which were circulating. When I have these men in mind, I am gripped by the thought of the anxiety, likewise well known to me, of the human creature before a truth which he fears he cannot face. But finally there appears before me, from reliable reports, some who have become as familiar to me by sight, action, and voice as if they were friends, those who refused to carry out the orders and suffered death or put themselves to death, and those who learned what was taking place and opposed it and were put to death, or those who learned what was taking place and because they could do nothing to stop it killed themselves. I see these men very near before me in that especial intimacy which binds us at times to the dead and to them alone. Reverence and love for these Germans now fills my heart.

But I must step out of memory into the present. Here I am surrounded by the youth who have grown up since those events and had no part in the great crime. These youth, who are probably the essential life of the German people today, show themselves to me in a powerful inner dialectic. Their core is included in the core of an inner struggle running for the most part underground and only occasionally coming to the surface. This is only a part, though one of the clearest, of the great inner struggle of all peoples being fought out today, more or less consciously, more or less passionately, in the vital center of each people.

The preparation for the final battle of *homo humanus*

against *homo contrahumanus* has begun in the depths. But the front is split into as many individual fronts as there are peoples, and those who stand on one of the individual fronts know little or nothing of the other fronts. Darkness still covers the struggle, upon whose course and outcome it depends whether, despite all, a true humanity can issue from the race of men. The so-called cold war between two gigantic groups of states with all its accompaniments still obscures the true obligation and solidarity of combat, whose line cuts right through all states and peoples, however they name their regimes. The recognition of the deeper reality, of the true need and the true danger, is growing. In Germany, and especially in German youth, despite their being rent asunder, I have found more awareness of it than elsewhere. The memory of the twelve-year reign of *homo contrahumanus* has made the spirit stronger, and the task set by the spirit clearer, than they formerly were.

Tokens such as the bestowal of the Hanseatic Goethe Prize and the Peace Prize of the German Book Trade on a surviving arch-Jew must be understood in this connection. They, too, are moments in the struggle of the human spirit against the demonry of the subhuman and the anti-human. The survivor who is the object of such honors is taken up into the high duty of solidarity that extends across the fronts: the solidarity of all separate groups in the flaming battle for the rise of a true humanity. This duty is, in the present hour, the highest duty on earth. The Jew chosen as symbol must obey this call of duty even there, indeed, precisely there where the never-to-be-effaced memory of what has happened stands in opposition to it. When he recently expressed his gratitude to the spirit of Goethe, victoriously disseminated throughout the world, and when he now expresses his gratitude to the spirit of peace, which now as so often before speaks to the world in books of the German tongue, his thanks signify his confession of solidarity with the common battle—common also to Germans and Jews—against the contrahuman, and his reply to a vow taken by fighters, a vow he has heard.

Hearkening to the human voice, where it speaks forth unfalsified, and replying to it, this above all is needed today. The busy noise of the hour must no longer drown out the *vox humana,* the essence of the human which has become a voice. This voice must not only be listened to, it must be answered and led out of the lonely monologue into the awakening dialogue of the peoples. Peoples must engage in talk with one another through their truly human men if the great peace is to appear and the devastated life of the earth renew itself.

The great peace is something essentially different from the absence of war.

In an early mural in the town hall of Siena the civic virtues are assembled. Worthy, and conscious of their worth, the women sit there, except one in their midst who towers above the rest. This woman is marked not by dignity but rather by composed majesty. Three letters announce her name: Pax. She represents the great peace I have in mind. This peace does not signify that what men call war no longer exists now that it holds sway—that means too little to enable one to understand this serenity. Something new exists, now really exists, greater and mightier than war, greater and mightier even than war. Human passions flow into war as the waters into the sea, and war disposes of them as it likes. But these passions must enter into the great peace as ore into the fire that melts and transforms it. Peoples will then build with one another with more powerful zeal than they have ever destroyed one another.

The Sienese painter had glimpsed this majestic peace in his dream alone. He did not acquire the vision from historical reality, for it has never appeared there. What in history has been called peace has never, in fact, been aught other than an anxious or an illusory blissful pause between wars. But the womanly genius of the painter's dream is no mistress of interruptions but the queen of new and greater deeds.

May we, then, cherish the hope that the countenance which has remained unknown to all previous history will shine forth on our late generation, apparently sunk irretrievably in disaster? Are we not accustomed to describe the world situation in which we have lived since the end of the Second World War no longer even as peace but as the "cold" phase of a world war declared in permanence? In a situation which no longer even seeks to preserve the appearance of peace, is it not illusory enthusiasm to speak of a great peace which has never existed being within reach?

It is the depth of our crisis that allows us to hope in this way. Ours is not an historically familiar malady in the life of peoples which can eventuate in a comfortable recovery. Primal forces are now being summoned to take an active part in an unrepeatable decision between extinction and rebirth. War has not produced this crisis; it is, rather, the crisis of man which has brought forth the total war and the unreal peace which followed.

War has always had an adversary who hardly ever comes forward as such but does his work in the stillness. This adversary is speech, fulfilled speech, the speech of genuine conversation in which men understand one another and come to a mutual understanding. Already in primitive warfare fighting begins where speech has ceased; that is, where men are no longer able to discuss with one another the subjects under dispute or submit them to mediation, but flee from speech with one another and in the speechlessness of slaughter seek what they suppose to be a decision, a judgment of God. War soon conquers speech and enslaves it in the service of its battle-cries. But where speech, be it ever so shy, moves from camp to camp, war is already called in question. Its cannons easily drown out the word; but when the word has become entirely soundless, and on this side and on that soundlessly bears into the hearts of men the intelligence that no human conflict can really be resolved through killing, not even through mass killing, then the human word has already begun to silence the cannonade.

But it is just the relation of man to speech and to conversation that the crisis characteristic of our age has in particular tended to shatter. The man in crisis will no longer entrust his cause to conversation because its presupposition—trust—is lacking. This is the reason why the cold war which today goes by the name of peace has been able to overcome mankind. In every earlier period of peace the living word has passed between man and man, time after time drawing the poison from the antagonism of interests and convictions so that these antagonisms have not degenerated into the absurdity of "no-farther" into the madness of "must-wage-war." This living word of human dialogue that from time to time makes its flights until the madness smothers it, now seems to have become lifeless in the midst of the non-war. The debates between statesmen which the radio conveys to us no longer have anything in common with a human conversation: the diplomats do not address one another but the faceless public. Even the congresses and conferences which convene in the name of mutual understanding lack the substance which alone can elevate the deliberations to genuine talk: candor and directness in address and answer. What is concentrated there is only the universal condition in which men are no longer willing or no longer able to speak directly to their fellows. They are not able to speak directly because they no longer trust one another, and everybody knows that the other no longer trusts him. If anyone in the hubbub of contradictory talk happens to pause and take stock, he discovers that in his relations to others hardly anything persists that deserves to be called trust.

And yet this must be said again and again, it is just the depth of the crisis that empowers us to hope. Let us dare to grasp the situation with that great realism that surveys all the definable realities of public life, of which, indeed, public life appears to be composed, but is also aware of what is most real of all, albeit moving secretly in the depths—the latent healing and salvation in the face of impending ruin. The power of turning that radically changes the situation, never reveals itself outside of crisis. This power begins to function when one, gripped by despair, instead of allowing himself to be submerged, calls forth his primal powers and accomplishes with them the turning of his very existence. It happens in this way both in the life of the person and in that of the race. In its depths the crisis demands naked decision: no mere fluctuation between getting worse and getting better, but a decision between the decomposition and the renewal of the tissue.

The crisis of man which has become apparent in our day announces itself most clearly as a crisis of trust, if we may employ, thus intensified, a concept of economics. You ask, trust in whom? But the question already contains a limitation not admissible here. It is simply trust that is increasingly lost to men of our time. And the crisis of speech is bound up with this loss of trust in the closest possible fashion, for I can only speak to someone in the true sense of the term if I expect him to accept my word as genuine. Therefore, the fact that it is so difficult for present-day man to pray (note well: not to hold it to be true that there is a God, but to address Him) and the fact that it is so difficult for him to carry on a genuine talk with his fellow-men are elements of a single set of facts. This lack of trust in Being, this incapacity for unreserved intercourse with the other, points to an innermost sickness of the sense of existence. One symptom of this sickness, and the most acute of all, is the one from which I have begun: that a genuine word cannot arise between the camps.

Can such an illness be healed? I believe it can be. And it is out of this, my belief, that I speak to you. I have no proof for this belief. No belief can be proved; otherwise it would not be what it is, a great venture. Instead of offering proof, I appeal to that potential belief of each of my hearers which enables him to believe.

If there be a cure, where can the healing action start? Where must that existential turning begin which the healing powers, the powers of salvation in the ground of the crisis, await?

That peoples can no longer carry on authentic dialogue with one another is not only the most acute symptom of the pathology of our time, it is also that which most urgently makes a demand of us. I believe, despite all, that the peoples in this hour can enter into dialogue, into a genuine dialogue with one another. In a genuine dialogue each of the partners, even when he stands in opposition to the other, heeds, affirms, and confirms his opponent as an existing other. Only so can conflict certainly not be eliminated from the world, but be humanly arbitrated and led toward its overcoming.

To the task of initiating this conversation those are inevitably called who carry on today within each people the battle against the anti-human. Those who build the great unknown front across mankind shall make it known by speaking unreservedly with one another, not overlooking what divides them but determined to bear this division in common.

In opposition to them stands the element that profits from the divisions between the peoples, the contra-human in men, the subhuman, the enemy of man's will to become a true humanity.

The name Satan means in Hebrew the hinderer. That is the correct designation for the anti-human in individuals and in the human race. Let us not allow this Satanic element in men to hinder us from realizing man! Let us release speech from its ban! Let us dare, despite all, to trust!

*(This address by Martin Buber concluded
the Peace Prize ceremony.)*

Martin Buber ❦ BOOKS AND PEOPLE

IF SOMEONE HAD ASKED ME IN MY EARLY YOUTH WHETHER I would prefer to associate only with people or only with books, I would surely have declared myself in favor of the latter. Later this changed more and more. Not that the experiences I had with people were so much better than those I had with books; on the contrary, even today I encounter entirely pleasant books far more frequently than entirely pleasant people. But the many bad experiences I have had with people have nourished my life's marrow in a way that the most exquisite book could not, and my good experiences with them have turned the earth into a garden for me.

On the other hand, no book can do more for me than transport me to a paradise of exalted spirits, where my heart of hearts never forgets that I am not permitted to stay for long and that I cannot even desire such permission. For, and I must say it right out to be understood, my heart of hearts loves the world more than it loves the intellect.

True, I am not as fit for living with the world as I would like to be: again and again I fail in my dealings with it; again and again I fall short of what it expects of me, and part of the reason is that I am so bound to the intellect. In a way, I am as much bound to it as I am bound to myself; but I do not really love it, just as I do not really love myself. Actually, I do not love this one that has seized me with its celestial claw and holds me fast, but the thing over there that keeps coming up and holding out a few fingers to me, the "world."

Both of them have gifts to distribute. The intellect gives me its manna: books; the world has dark bread for me on whose crust I loosen my teeth and with which I am never sated: people. Oh, these muddle-heads and ne'er-do-wells, how I love them! I respect books—those that I really read—far too much to be able to love them that way. But in the most respected living person I always get a bit more to love than to respect, always a bit of this world, which is simply there in a way that the intellect can never be there.

True, it is above me and "exists," but it is not there. It hovers over me powerfully and talks down at me with its exalted words, the books; how magnificent, how uncanny! The world of men, however, needs only to smile its mute smile and I cannot live without it.

It is mute, for all the talk of people does not add up to a word such as I derive from books time and time again. And I put up with all that talk in order to be able to hear the silence that comes through, the muteness of created things. But it is that of *human* creatures! Which means, that of a mixture. Books are pure, people are mixed; books are spirit and word, pure spirit and purified words; people are put together out of talk and muteness, and the muteness is not that of animals, but that of men, and lo, out of human muteness behind the talk the spirit whispers to you, the spirit as *soul*. This, this is the beloved.

There is an infallible test. Try to imagine a primeval situation in which you are alone, all alone on earth, and you could get one of the two, books or people. Yes, I can hear some praising their solitude; but they are able to do that only because there *are* people in the world, even though far away in space. I knew nothing of books when I sprang from my mother's womb, and I want to die without books, with a human hand clasping mine. Now, to be sure, I sometimes close the door of my room and surrender to a book, but only because I can open the door again and see a human being looking up at me.

Albrecht Goes ✤ ENCOUNTER IN HUNGARY

IT HAPPENED EARLY IN 1944 WHEN WE HAD ESCAPED THE POLISH winter, that hard, gray-white winter. Our marching orders had taken us to Hungary, and we regarded that as a sort of salvation in the face of the Russian Armies that were forging ahead toward Lov. We had been marching for only ten days, and already it seemed to us as if we were on another star. Back there, the Easter morning had still brought snow, but here, these first days of May, it was already summer, the Hungarian kind, with jubilation and exuberance, blossoms in every garden, colors in every lane, gaiety under the sky. This gaiety, to be sure, was not unmuted, not unencumbered, even here—that we noticed soon enough. The Magyars all around us looked at us more than a little frightened; no matter whether we came as friends or foes—this wasn't such a sure thing as the rulers of nations might believe. What were we up to and what were we bringing with us? British air raids, most likely; and when would the Red Army be at the Dukla Pass?

It was then, too, that we encountered Jews again for the first time, well-dressed Jews; you could tell them from ten paces away. For here, too, the mark of hell, the Yellow Star, had just been introduced. We were to take lodgings in a good-sized town; this Tisza valley countryside seemed to be a wine and grain paradise. A headquarters was established and there was an order reserving some rooms for us in the better Jewish

30

houses. "11 Sandor Petöfi Street," it said on my room ticket, and under it there was the name of Dr. Lajos. I set out, found my way, thinking of Petöfi, the Hungarian Goethe, and made a mental resolve to become acquainted with his works. Number 11: first there was nothing but a bare wall, one story high, and a high gate into a courtyard and garden—nothing inviting at first glance. But scarcely had I set foot inside the gate when I saw a well-kept garden area and a stately house whose windows and doors faced the lilies and rose bushes. I climbed some stairs and stood at the threshold. The door opened and two men confronted me: father and son, I could tell immediately, the owners of the house, both of them physicians, as the name plate informed me. "Good afternoon." Rather shyly we exchanged greetings and our names and titles. Communication was possible. The Jews are almost the only people in this part of the country who speak German. They heard what my profession was and the older one got up enough courage to say: "We are very glad to have a clergyman in the house from now on." A small bow. We hadn't been given any orders as to how to behave—and what could such instructions have meant? In such situations every one acts according to the mode of his inner life.

They led me into the room assigned to me. A very big, impersonal one, with a dark, cold elegance. Strange—in this very first hour everything tasted of break-up, farewell, finish. I shivered in the middle of the radiant day. A beautiful green carpet covered almost the entire floor; the wooden wardrobes were massive, old, and dark; they were locked and seemed to be full. My orderly arrived; we made ourselves at home after a fashion. There was actually no room even for our hosts' things; books stood on the marble top of a side-board. Schwinghammer, ever the helpful soldier, found fault with this situation in no uncertain terms. As for me, I found myself unable even to express a wish in this house, let alone to issue commands or make arbitrary rearrangements. "We'll have to make shift this way," I said; "it'll be all right."

Within an hour we had taken care of the essentials. A big,

golden stream of light came in through the window now, late light, for it was toward evening. There was a knock at the door. "Come in, please." The two doctors appeared: the father a septuagenarian, it would seem, but of the robust vigor of his race, with big, dark, painfully veiled eyes; the son taller than his father by a head, with softer features, a man about my age. They wondered whether everything was to my liking and asked me to express any wish I might have. "We want the Reverend to feel at home here." I muttered something about clearing off a shelf in the wardrobe for my linen. "Oh, hasn't that been done yet? It is an oversight. You must excuse it. There is no woman in this house—I mean, there is only a housekeeper who comes in for a few hours each day. I am a widower and my son is not married yet. Tomorrow we'll make room. Certainly, that must be done. You must pardon us." I spoke a few phrases of courtesy, some words of thanks. Now the two walked backwards toward the door, somewhat indecisively.

Suddenly there was a question in the room; I knew that it would come. "Reverend, you will protect us, won't you?" Good Lord, what a question! What an idea! All of us knew, each in his way, what was meant by that question. We knew that very different outfits would move in after us, hard at our heels. Not medics, but murder commandos. The outrage of the pogroms —how much longer would it be delayed? A month perhaps, or two at the most. And I was supposed to protect them? A touching expectation, an oppressing thought.

What was I to reply? I said: "I am part of the Red Cross. You know that we are medics. No harm will come to you from us." Phrases. Excuses. They knew it as well as I did.

They started in again: "As you see, we have to wear the Yellow Star now when we go out into the street. There will be restrictions on our medical practice and otherwise. We fear that all this is only the beginning of worse things—we don't know . . ."

Oh, of course, they didn't know. But how about us? Did we know? No, we didn't know much either. To be sure, we were coming from the Ukraine; we had heard terrible, unspeakable things—from a distance only, but still close enough. The memory of wakeful nights in the typhoid fever ward came to me, the confessions of men crazed by the fever. I remembered the delirious ravings of an S.S. man who had always worn such a crafty expression whenever I entered the little sickroom in the days when his illness was still in its first stages. Then the fever, that red fire-bell, had come over him, and he had cried his snatches of sentences into the sick night—let one put them together in any way he would: "Don't—don't—please don't shoot—stop—but I always helped—." And then: "Undress—naked—naked women—lie down—face down." It was but a vision in this twilight hour in Hungary in May. A minute of horror . . . a picture by Hieronymus Bosch.

There they stood. Father and son. Physicians, both of them. Intelligent faces, sorrowful countenances. Jews. Verses rushed in upon me, Franz Werfel's verses about Jewish fate:

> So I, with no people, no land,
> prop my face in my hand.

The light was taking leave of the day. It was dark-golden, something only seldom to be seen in Germany. The cupola of the synagogue could probably be discerned from the spot where I was standing. It occurred to me that in this country being a Jew has always been tantamount to being an Israelite, with membership in the Old Covenant and Law. I was thinking of Moses, of David, of Jeremiah, again and again of Jeremiah. And then I suddenly broke the silence with

Shema Yisroel, adonoi elohenu, adonoi echod—

the old "Hear, O Israel, the Lord our God is One," the words which they once put on their wrists, the solemn words of their covenant, of theirs and of ours.

This is what happened now: hardly had I spoken these words, hardly had these Hebrew sounds died away in this room in Hungary, when the two men were rocked by emotion.

There were tears in the father's eyes, and the son looked at me ardently and visibly shaken. They came up to me and pressed my hand. What had once been strangeness and fear had sunk away. The Lord our God is One.

THREE NOVELS OF EXPIATION

Albrecht Goes ❦ **UNQUIET NIGHT**

[1]

DURING THE WHOLE OF SEPTEMBER I HAD NOT MANAGED TO LEAVE
the town. And it had been a particularly fine, warm September, just the sort of weather to tempt an old rambler out for
long walks through the open countryside. But I had had no
choice; my duties as pastor responsible for the spiritual welfare
of the troops in the district fully occupied each day. First were
the hospitals, then my periodic visits to the soldiers' barracks
and billets, not to mention the prisoners in the army prison,
and, of course, the military cemetery. This latter dated from
the short, sharp battle of Vinnitsa in July, '41, and during the
subsequent fifteen months it had been enlarged at an appall-
ing rate. Now the late flowers that decked those graves were
withering, and if I wished to see anything of the brilliant
Ukrainian autumn I should have to hurry, for in these parts
the end of October is often the beginning of winter.

So I decided not to let slip by another deep-blue, wind-swept
October day. Of course it was a civilian emotion, and as such a
thoroughly scandalous one, this longing of mine for the open
road, for the smell of the bonfires and the sight of the sunflower fields, for the light on the rich black soil, and for a

37

peaceful hour passed alone on the bank of the river Bug. A proper soldier simply does his duty and in the evening goes to the pictures or drinks vodka or visits his girl, but in this, as in so many other matters, I had never become a proper soldier. "You're a hopeless case," Staff Doctor Dold had recently said to me when I had told him how I found myself, hurrying down a wide street at night, reciting Homer aloud.

Be that as it may, all I cared about was that I should succeed in saving a fair portion of this richly scented, balmy, autumn day, with its fast-moving white clouds, and should manage to make of it something decent and worthwhile. It would be best, I decided, to take the morning off. Dinner was at twelve-thirty, and for the Prussian, eating his meals forms part of his military duties—a compulsory half-hour spent in the officers' mess with an attempted expression of maximum politeness on his face. So that would mark the end of my marvelous freedom; meanwhile the morning would be given over to it.

Besides, there was nothing special happening in the hospital that required my presence. I had been informed by telephone that the stomach wound delivered the night before had died at five-thirty A.M. I had looked in on him late at night, but he had still been only semi-conscious, as he had been ever since his arrival by ambulance. (I feel that I should apologize at this point for using the hospital jargon by which wounded men are referred to as "the femur" or "the lung wound," so that one hears phrases such as "the ulcer in 26 is being put on a special diet." It is a frightful way of talking, and I shall do my best to avoid it.) In any event, the man with the stomach wound, who had been a fair-haired Westphalian, was dead. It would be time enough this afternoon to find out his home address from his paybook, and to write one of those sad letters which it was my duty to compose.

I would not think of that now. The paved road had come to an end. When one reached the sugar factory one was already without the town limits, and beyond it the true open country began. Here were no more ruins, no poverty, no smashed windows, no shabbiness; here the world was healthy, as it may have been intended to be on the day of creation, healthy, wide and good. The earth was an indescribably rich brown, tinged with a purplish shimmer. Over there the river flowed by, a clear boundary, with scarce a bend, hardly a reed to break its even surface, and only an occasional willow bending over its bank. On the higher land beyond stood the old monastery and church; the many onion-shaped domes, which from close to resembled nothing so much as a strange collection of exotic bulbs, now glistened gloriously, white and gold in the rays of the morning sun.

I hurried. It was as though by walking through this countryside I were making it mine. There was no sound save for the soughing of the high wind, no voice but my own. Now that there was no one to hear, I could at last talk aloud: Blessed be the autumn! Blessed be freedom! Though freedom in this flat countryside was not altogether without its dangers, as I well knew. Solitary walks were definitely discouraged by the authorities. Since the application of a ruthless policy of land exploitation, and the revelation that all the talk about liberation had been only a mixture of lies and hot air, the partisans had got to work. From month to month they grew more daring and successful. In the hospital we were bound to realize this, for never a week passed but a wounded soldier was brought in. So be it. I intended to go on all the same, to give myself over to the wild wind. I should go as far as the sunflower field which I could see up ahead, and then, taking the path to the right, come back by way of the bank of the Bug.

Of course, something was bound to have turned up back there, and they'd be hunting for me all over the place. Well, let them look, I'd be back soon enough. The model prisoner returns to his cell unsummoned.

What time was it? Close to half-past eleven, which meant that there would be just time to stop by the prison and find out quickly whether there were any new developments in the Rothweiler business. Lieutenant Rothweiler had been handed

over to us the day before, after an unsuccessful attempt at suicide; he had tried to cut the veins in his wrists. It was an unpleasant story. He had already been under arrest for four
weeks on a charge of self-inflicted wounds. I believed him to be
innocent on that score, and I thought I had good reasons for
that belief. Now, by this last act of his, he had proved himself
to be his own enemy and had destroyed all chance of rehabili-
tation. Suicide must succeed, or else it leads only to trouble
and worse than trouble. This was war, and in war a man may
not live as he wishes. As for his having any choice as to how
and when he dies, that is absolutely out of the question.

There was the stream. Geese and wild duck flew up, the
damp wind flicked at the silvery ripples, it was beautiful, it
was peace. No, I should not visit the prison, not yet. These
hours would be entirely given over to what is good. The officers' mess would be prison enough. So I took the direct road to
the hospital, passing through the main gate at exactly twelve-
fifteen. There I met the ophthalmologist, who had just left his
office, and who said cheerfully, rubbing his hands, "Lunch
time!"

The duty private stopped me.

"The staff sergeant-major asks the chaplain to be so good as
to come to his office immediately, sir."

The orderly room was down the hall on the far side. Before I
could reach it Staff Sergeant-major Hirzel, who must have seen
me coming, stepped out. He said, and I could detect a tone of
disapproval in his voice, "We've been looking for you for a
long time, sir."

Naturally, I thought to myself, half amused and half annoyed: it's too much to expect to live one's own life for four
whole hours. I asked:

"What's up then?"

"This signal's come in from Proskurov."

"Well, well. What do they want?"

"It's urgent. We had to send an answer in your name at
once."

I read:

*Senior area command Proskurov requires prot. chaplain.
Should arrive not later seventeen hundred hours Wednesday.
Report Dept. III. Proskurov will provide armored transport
vehicle. Return Thursday envisaged.*

Wednesday was today.

"We approved it from here," said Hirzel. "The car from
Proskurov is on the way. You're to leave at fourteen hundred,
so you'll be in plenty of time."

"I see."

I was only half listening to what he was saying. Department
III was the legal department of all military headquarters. So I
knew the meaning of this summons. I was to assist at a military
execution.

"Very well, Sergeant-major. Thank you." All I added was,
"Have you informed the C.O.?"

"Yes, he just stopped by."

"Good."

"A pleasant dinner, padre!"

"Thank you, and the same to you."

I hurried up the stairs and, without even going to my room,
made my way straight to the mess in the hope of getting there
before the C.O., the senior staff doctor, arrived. But they had
already begun to eat. There was nothing for it but to go to the
head of the table and murmur my apologies.

The C.O. glanced up from his soup.

"Did Hirzel get hold of you?"

"Yes, sir, I've just been talking to him."

"Aha! Sounds like an unpleasant job."

"I think so too. I don't quite understand why they're sending for me. Proskurov has its own chaplains' section, I know."

"I don't understand, either. Hirzel couldn't get through on
the phone. Well, you'll see soon enough."

And with that the meal relapsed into its customary silence.
My Catholic colleague, Klaus, with whom I would willingly
have had a word, was seated far away. My place was next to

Jessen, the intern, and he was summoned by telephone on urgent business immediately after the soup.

Coffee was served at two round tables in a big bay window; here smoking was permitted, and from time to time an attempt was even made at conversation. Today I could not stay for this, since I would have to hurry if I were to be packed and ready to leave at fourteen hundred, that is to say in an hour's time.

"May I have permission to dismiss, sir?"

The C.O. stood up, holding out as was his custom two fingers of his narrow hand, and he looked at me through half-closed eyes as he said, "Well, enjoy yourself."

And with these words he turned his back on me and made his way goutily across to the coffee table.

One-fifteen. There were some letters in my room, and I shoved them unread into my briefcase—human words in this inhuman present. This was no time for reading, smiling, loving. . . .

I unhooked the telephone.

"Orderly room, please."

"Orderly room, sir? Yes, sir."

"Orderly room speaking, Private Weik."

"Good afternoon, Weik. Listen, I want my movement order right away."

"It's all made out, but I can't bring it up to you. There's no one else here."

"Right. I'll come down and get it."

Get the movement order, draw my haversack rations: bread, lard, tinned sausage meat, a little roll of fruit drops. All these actions I performed automatically, like running off thread from a giant spool. How often had I not done all this before? and how often would I do it again? As I hurried down a long corridor with my rations in my hand it struck me like a flash of nightmare: for a thousand days—I calculated rapidly, yes, that was correct—for a thousand days now this had all been going on. Here, behind these doors, men had lain and groaned and loved and died. Letters had been written, games played, chess, halma, draughts, skat, pinochle. Injections were given, cardial, intravenal, subcutaneous. Leave rosters were drawn up and canceled. Men drank, smoked, swore. Seven hands wrote sick reports for the perusal of the gentlemen in the Medical Inspector's office on a disturbance to the circulatory system or twenty-four hours *exitus letalis*. Lists were made out, lists of arrivals, lists of departures, pay lists and lists of partial payments. Paper was piled on paper, enough to build a new tower of Babel. Sometimes a nurse would pass down the ward. There was one, a girl in her first youth and of great beauty, who already wore two wedding rings on her right hand. Dear God, a girl, a human being. . . .

What was there still to do? First I must decide what I would need on my trip. My night things, the Bible as reading material, the various objects needed for celebration of Holy Communion, two candles, and cigarettes, plenty of cigarettes, for they are always useful. And already the telephone was ringing.

"Chaplain, sir, the car from Proskurov is here."

I knocked rapidly at Klaus' door, but he was not in his room. He was presumably engaged in his usual post-prandial chess game with either the surgeon or the chemist. A pity, for I would have liked to have a word with him to take with me on my journey. He knew what it meant to be summoned to an execution; and I had no doubt that I was on my way to take part in one.

So now, for the second time that day, I found myself traveling across that countryside, though now I was going at great speed along paved roads. Vinnitsa soon dropped out of sight, and so did the trusted country that I knew so well. For a good hour we drove without seeing a single house, with only here and there an occasional huge granary rising solitary in the open fields, and then once again the endless expanse of sunflowers, myriads of them, a veritable sea of golden, warmth-giving oil.

I should have liked to question my driver, a broad-shouldered fellow from Hamburg, about the route. But he was taci-

turn and unresponsive, and I felt that he resented the whole
journey. Doubtless he had had to miss a good time on account
of it. Perhaps he had already turned into one of those stubborn-
minded old soldiers who do everything and nothing: everything that is ordered and nothing that is not.

The Turkish Castle came in sight. I had heard of it and read
about it too, and now there it stood, massive bastion of the
middle ages. It did not lie directly in our path, though it was
hardly more than three miles off our route. I suggested we
make a short detour in order to look at it, but it was clear that
the driver didn't want to do so. He glanced anxiously at his
wrist watch, muttering something about the road being a bad
one and the orders he had to take me direct to the Area Command.

Well, it was a pity. Now I know that I shall never go there.
Occasionally in my mind's eye I see an exact image of that
tower, and I think: Once, in October of nineteen forty-two, I
drove straight past that place. Such is war. So it would happen
that a man, being transferred from the Eastern Front to the
West, will pass through his home town without so much as
being able to leave the train. He would be standing at the
window in the corridor, looking out, and there he would suddenly see opposite him the balcony of his home. Perhaps if he
was in luck his wife might be hanging out the washing, and he
could catch a glimpse of her red dress and her black hair.

I was sunk deep in thought, and I had not noticed that we
were now driving past houses. "Here we are," the driver said
suddenly, though without looking at me. I handed him the
customary tip, two cigarettes, he thanked me unenthusiasti-
cally and opened the door for me without a word.

[2]

AN ARMED SENTRY WAS POSTED OUTSIDE THE HEADQUARTERS
building of the Area Command, so presumably some fairly dis-

tinguished individual lived in there, perhaps even a real live general. I went in and, as is customary, made my way at once to the adjutant's office. On the door was a card: *Dept. IIa, Major Kartuschke.*

Every office exudes its own peculiar atmosphere. A man in my position inevitably passed through so many of them that he soon became particularly sensitive to their varying qualities. I had plenty of opportunity in this way to study racial and environmental characteristics, to learn the distinctions between North and South Germans, to differentiate between Bavarian and Austrian. I could quickly estimate whether and how much the man in charge of the office was a Hitlerite, even as an oenophilist can judge at one sip the quality of the wine that is set before him.

"The major is in conference," said the orderly room corporal.

The atmosphere in this office struck me immediately as unpleasant. Our orderly room up in Vinnitsa was at least a bit fresher than this, though politeness and cheerfulness were not conspicuous even there: indeed, what was there to be cheerful about? But this office I didn't care for at all. I turned toward the door, beneath the hostile stare of one of the two privates seated among mounds of papers; before the door closed behind me, I heard this soldier mutter to the corporal, "Conference is a new word for it!"

During those long years we all made surprising progress in at least one subject: we learned quickly to grasp the half-meaning and covert allusions in any remark we heard. It was impossible to be ten minutes in that army without becoming conscious of the all-enveloping, slimy filth. And I sometimes wonder whether, even if we should recover from the ravages of that war, we shall ever succeed in sweeping our brains clear of those double meanings, those brothel fantasies.

But that is irrelevant now. I was in a hurry as I hastened along the corridors of this dingy paperwork palace, this temple dedicated to the tattered idols of forms and files. At last I found the correct door, with a Roman three and the words *Legal Officer* on it. Justice in jackboots. What next?

There he was, the legal officer himself. He jumped to his feet, told me his name—which I failed to catch—and offered me a seat. Then he began to speak, quickly and formally.

"I much regret the inconvenience to which we must have put you in asking you to come here; but our local Department IVa is at present not up to establishment and we have no Protestant chaplain available. The prisoner, Fedor Baranowski, was found guilty of desertion by a field general court-martial and sentenced to death. We were informed yesterday afternoon that the General Officer Commander-in-Chief Ukraine has dismissed the prisoner's appeal. In accordance with standing operational procedure the sentence must be carried out within forty-eight hours. In consequence the execution by shooting will take place at o-five-forty-five hours tomorrow in the sand quarry behind the brickworks. In accordance with para. sixteen of the relevant standing orders, the condemned man is entitled to the presence of a chaplain of his faith. Since, as I say, the Protestant chaplain normally attached to this organization is temporarily not available, I was instructed by my superiors to send for you forthwith. I should like to thank you for coming."

He said his piece as though he were reading aloud from a document, and he spoke in a curiously cold, flat tone. But that is the customary manner of expression among such men. Automatically, I found myself answering in the same manner.

"When dealing with prisoners, and particularly with prisoners under sentence of death, I always attempt as best I can to establish a personal relationship with the man. If my work has any sense at all, it cannot possibly start at the place of execution. Therefore in this case, too, I should like to learn as much as I possibly can about the man and about what he has done."

The legal officer, in a voice that was now a shade less inhuman, replied, "It's left entirely up to you to decide how best you can perform your duties."

I looked at the clock. It was a quarter to six.

"First of all I should like, briefly, to make the prisoner's acquaintance. Then I should be grateful if you would be so good as to let me have the documents dealing with his case so that I might study them this evening."

"It's not customary to let documents out of this office. Here, of course, you're at perfect liberty . . . However . . . Schmitt!"

An orderly appeared.

"The Baranowski folder."

"The Baranowski folder? Yes, sir!"

The documents were brought in. They comprised a fairly thick bundle, which was so carefully tied up with string that only one conclusion was possible: so far as this department was concerned, the man was already dead.

"A great deal of paper, I'm afraid," the legal officer said. "A lot for you to read. As I say, we don't usually allow our documents to be taken out of this building, but I realize that the circumstances are unusual. You may take the folder with you, but please realize that you will be held personally responsible for its safe keeping."

"Of course."

"I shall have to have a receipt in writing."

"Yes, naturally."

As I was signing the receipt, I asked, "Where is your prison here?"

"Go down the main street about three hundred yards and you'll see it on the other side, a low building. It's not really a prison, but more a sort of glorified guardroom. Ask for Sergeant-major Mascher."

"Sergeant-major Mascher, thank you. Thank you very much."

"Not at all. Good-bye, padre. I shall be at the prison at about five-fifteen tomorrow morning to read the sentence to the condemned man. That should give us plenty of time."

"Yes . . . I'll be there before you."

"Till tomorrow then."

I took the documents and put them in my briefcase, which I

locked. And that was that. Such was the Legal Department, Proskurov Area Command. What is there to say about it? At best only that phrase which was really quite a high compliment as one was shunted hither and thither in wartime: it might have been worse. It was bad enough, in all conscience, if one stopped to think about it. The legal officer hadn't troubled to say one single word about the man who was to die by shooting at dawn next day, a man of flesh and blood, of hopes and fears, of sorrow and anguish. But that was the way it went. And now what could I anticipate from the adjutant, provided, of course, that he had returned from his ominous conference?

I entered the orderly room without knocking. Yes, he was there now, standing beside the door that led into his private office, a short, thickset man of about forty-five, holding a piece of paper in his hand.

"Heil Hitler, padre!"

Which was unambiguously offensive. He went on, "I gather you've already seen the legal officer. So you know what the score is. Extreme unction tonight and curtains tomorrow."

I made no reply. I looked into his eyes for a moment and then, for horror and for shame, I had to glance away. It is horrible that there should be men who have no right to exist. This was one of them.

"Nasty sort of job, yours, God knows!" he said. "A nice warm bed with a pretty girl in it would be better, eh, Schrotz?"

He turned toward one of his clerks, the third man, who up to now had kept his head buried in his papers, and had not looked up either this time or during my previous visit to this room. Now he raised his eyes, and as I looked at him I realized, in the flash of a second, that this wretched building, this foul office, could yet contain a human being. His whole expression was one of serious nobility, and also of sadness, as he looked from the major to me. He did not speak.

His silence annoyed the major. Throwing the document he was holding down onto the table he shouted:

"Stop pretending to be so pure! You've had plenty of girls in your time. . . ."

It was an intolerable situation. I was here to do a job—and what a job!—and this man, instead of talking to me as was his duty, chose to amuse himself with obscenities. It would be plain cowardice on my part were I not to walk out of his office at once.

What sort of creature was he? Where did he come from? How did he happen to hold a majority? This war was one vast explosion of hatred against the spiritual values of health and vitality, and in its treatment of men it produced the most absurd anomalies over and over again. A professor of philosophy would be made to count sides of bacon in an army supply depot, while a paymaster, who in real life had a sublime knowledge of Horace, spent his days issuing tables and chairs and scrub buckets; whereas a hairdresser who had played his cards correctly at the right time might by now well be a captain. But I couldn't make out what this Kartuschke might have been in the old days, in another world.

Meanwhile I had followed him into his private room, where he waved me toward a chair. I ignored his unspoken offer, and he said, "Let's skip all the phoney piety, shall we? When a man deserts he's asking for all he gets, and that's all there is to it. The rest is up to the firing squad. Victory will go to the strong, and the Führer has no time for yellowbellies."

Then, in a different tone, "You have your papers?"

I replied that I had, and that I intended to find out as soon as I could what the background to the man's desertion had been. He laughed disagreeably, and I discovered that he was not referring to the legal documents but to my billeting slip or something equally silly.

"Background!" He banged on the desk with his fist. "What do backgrounds matter nowadays? Psychological details, eh? For Christ's sake don't talk to me about psychology. To hell with it I say. No, no. All we need is a good, loud Lord's Prayer at dawn tomorrow, and then curtains, lights out. It's our duty to give the full strength of our support to the fighting troops. I'm afraid I've no time at all for sentimental half-wits.

"Now, to get back to your business . . ." he went on. But at that moment the door opened and the general appeared. Kartuschke stood up to attention, facing his commanding officer. The general wore his overcoat unbuttoned. He was a man in his sixties, with decorations from the First World War and the flushed, non-committal face of the habitual heavy drinker.

I had saluted, and I waited for the general to speak to me. Major Kartuschke made a gesture in my direction.

"The chaplain," he said. I felt he really might have been a little more polite. "The chaplain's here to officiate at the shooting of Baranowski at dawn tomorrow."

The general now addressed me.

"Where have you come from?"

"From Vinnitsa, sir."

"You're taking the place of . . . ?"

"Of Chaplain Holze."

"What's happened to Holze?" The question was directed at the major, who replied, "Holze's been relieved. We haven't had a replacement assigned yet."

"Oh yes, I remember now. That business about the funeral and the defeatist remarks. Yes, yes, an open-and-shut case. Everything ready for tomorrow? On occasions like this it's most disagreeable if anything goes wrong."

"A.G.O. is providing coffin and transport. Lieutenant Ernst of the Third Battalion 532 will command the firing squad. That's all there is to it."

(A.G.O. meant Army Graves Officer. The destruction of our language was being successfully carried out according to plan. Such a plan did exist. Men deprived of their language become as corpses, and corpses never disobey.)

There was no reply. The general began to button his coat as he turned to me once again. Say something, I thought, just say one real sentence; after all, you are wearing the uniform of Clausewitz! At last it came out.

"Well, try and see there's no hitch tomorrow."

Such was the sentence that I had been waiting for. No, on this ground, corn would never grow again. It was high time it were abandoned, plowed up, and left for the weeds and the thistles. It had already borne a crop of them, yes, and of poison berries too.

I said—and for the second time I tasted the bitter bile of my own cowardice—"Yes, sir."

The general nonchalantly touched the peak of his cap and went out. I imagine that my face must have expressed the overpowering sensation of nausea that afflicted me. If I did not get out into the fresh air soon I should suffocate. Perhaps even Kartuschke noticed my expression, for there was a definite note of sarcasm in his voice as he said, "Here's your billeting slip, chaplain."

I looked at the major once again. He was wearing the Iron Cross, both first and second class, as well as the Infantry Assault Badge, and the latter, I knew, was not given for nothing. He was utterly worthless, this officer, of that I was certain. Yet he was not a man without a history, without a chain of experience. Perhaps it was important to know that history, to understand that chain. That is why we call ourselves ministers. We are supposed to minister to everyone. To encourage a brave clerk like Schrotz to hold up his head, there was no difficulty in that. The coming interview with Baranowski tonight might well prove a harder task. But what was done for the Kartuschkes of the army? And what was left undone? By us, nothing and everything.

I left. I was offered a guide to show me the way to the Transit Officers' Billet, but I declined.

"Thank you. I'm sure I'll have no trouble finding it."

That was right. There was no reason for me to behave toward Kartuschke as though I were an N.C.O. On the other hand, the fact that I could not bring myself to shake hands with him before leaving I recognized, as soon as I was outside, for what it was: defeat.

[3]

NEXT CAME A SORT OF INTERLUDE, OF SOME THIRTY-FIVE MIN-
utes' duration, which might be entitled: In the Transit Billet.
Since I now knew the name of the chief protagonist in the
drama that was to be played out tonight and tomorrow, I was
very anxious to see him, and everything that delayed this encounter was to me a glassy, transparent barrier. Even my meeting with Kartuschke lost almost all semblance of reality as soon
as it was over. Fedor Baranowski. Words have their own mystery, but names are magical. I could not help it if from behind
this name—unknown to me an hour ago, already almost oblit-
erated from the tablets of history, and destined to remain forever obscure—another name should rise up, inextinguishable,
almost saintly, and yet terrifying too, in sound very close to
that of the deserter, the name of Feodor Dostoevski. At the very
last moment, on the scaffold itself, his life had been saved. But
the lieutenant's squad—what was he called? Lieutenant Ernst,
was it?—would not fail.

I hurried along the streets of the darkening town and suddenly realized that I had been paying no attention to the many
signposts and countless military directions that enabled one to
find one's way through the maze. I was almost beginning to
regret having declined the offer of a guide, when I became
aware of a smell of cooking and heard the clatter of pots and
pans. Perhaps this was it. The house had obviously been an
inn many years ago, one of those country inns with stables and
other outbuildings such as are described over and over again
in Russian novels, conjuring up a memory of the tinkling bells
of troikas, the smell of furs and brandy, the soft voices of heavily veiled women or the deep ones of grand dukes, the whole
web of fate. Now the local German military authorities had
requisitioned it and had turned it into the Transit Officers'
Billet, with an officers' mess and sleeping quarters. It was in
constant use, on account of the airfield just outside the town.

The establishment of such places was always the same; an invisible quartermaster would be technically responsible, while an elderly sergeant was actually in charge, with three or four soldiers under him who, in turn, gave orders to a dozen or so of the native inhabitants, kitchen maids, potato peelers, cleaning women and such. If they all managed to work well together the result would be tolerable, and even, on occasion, quite good.

There was no question of ostentation or splendor, of luxury or excess, in such places. The Prussian system demands only cold austerity and essential sufficiency. One's papers were carefully examined, a clear Yes or No was given to all questions, and the resultant rigid orderliness was, indeed, perhaps the best that one could hope for in the circumstances. No tinge of human warmth was to be expected, and should one somehow occur it was accepted by all as a rare and precious surprise.

I went into the office and explained what I wanted: that I should be leaving at about four the next morning, and that I had to have somewhere quiet to work during the night. "So you see it's essential that I have a room to myself."

"I'm sorry, sir, but I can't promise you that, padre. All our rooms have two or three beds in them, even the rooms reserved for the officers of the general staff. We get a great number of officers passing through here. I'll give you a room that is empty at the moment, and of course I'll do my best to see that you have it to yourself, but I can't promise. I may have to put somebody else in with you."

He spoke with unusual politeness, and in an accent, moreover, which I recognized.

"Where are you from?" I asked the lance-corporal with the pleasantly human voice.

"From Balingen in the Swabian Alps," he replied.

"From Balingen? In that case we're fellow countrymen."

I shook hands with him, asked after one or two people whom I knew, and had a short and agreeable conversation with the man. As so often during those years, I thought: Germany scarcely exists as a country any more, and the famous Greater Germany is nothing but a politician's pipe dream . . . but real roots, the feeling for a particular stretch of countryside, the local accent, the way of smiling, the climate, the same attitude toward time, the same methods of work—those do exist and they establish a true bond almost without effort.

My guide showed me the night entrance, where the key was left, and led me to my room. Like the rest of the establishment it was bare but clean; and since it was L-shaped, with a deep alcove in one wall, it was almost like two rooms. I decided to use the alcove as my sleeping quarters and to work in the main part of the room. I said, with a smile, "This isn't a room, it's a suite!"

"Not quite, padre sir," he replied, "but it's not bad. And if you'll tell me when you expect to be back. I'll see that the heating is on."

"Heating? That would really be splendid. Let me see. . . . I have to go out right away. I should be back by about half-past nine, say ten at the latest. By the way, is it possible for me to get something to eat here?"

"Supper's ready now."

The man from Balingen left me. I put my things away though I kept my briefcase with me when I went down to the dining room. This would not have seemed out of place in any little Swabian country town, and it was fairly full. I handed over my ticket, and helped myself. There was soup, vegetables and potatoes, an amply sufficient meal. Yet the atmosphere was most unpleasant, enveloping all the actors in this quite accidental reunion in a sort of miasma of awkwardness which no one seemed able to shake off. Could any enemy mess, say an American one, possibly be such a stifling place? Surely not. And in this connection I recalled one or two descriptions of such communal meals as Goethe gives in his *Campaign in France*. That again was another world, from which came an echo of human dignity and friendliness. Did not the great writer go so far as to say that there was no companionship more worthwhile than that of an educated military man?

True, I did recollect another passage in that journal which I had read so long ago. It was a description of a party of soldiers dining together at Treves, who looked "as though they were caught in a common hell." There was ample reason to be reminded of that passage in the Transit Officers' dining room at Proskurov.

No objective person could doubt that by this time—it was October, 1942—Hitler had lost all chance of winning his war. The German advance had been halted at Stalingrad, where fierce fighting was in progress; an Allied landing in North Africa was anticipated; and an English counterattack in the neighborhood of Tobruk seemed more than likely. That we must lose the war if there were to be hope of a decent life for us in the future—that was an idea which at that time had only occurred to a few isolated individuals. We were mainly preoccupied by day to day matters, the unnecessary discomforts of our life as soldiers, the lengthy cancellations of all leave, the dreary, unending spectacle of toadying and favoritism, and from time to time the evil rumors from home. Despite an attempt at utmost secrecy, news had leaked out about the mass extermination of the mentally unfit, and apart from those responsible an occasional individual did know more than he could bear about the Jewish pogroms.

Without being in any way sumptuous, our evening meal was good and well cooked. Trains were still crossing the frontiers, more or less unmolested, with their cargoes of wheat and sugar and oil, and the plump soldiers in cushy jobs at the rear certainly lacked for nothing. Yet a heavy cloud of gloom seemed to hang over our dining room. Did this not prove that deception concerning the reality of the situation could not last much longer? Did it not bear witness to a harsh and menacing truth: what is ill-gotten cannot thrive?

[4]

I HAD DELIBERATELY NOT TELEPHONED THE PRISON TO SAY THAT
I was coming. It was necessary for me to get a clear picture of
what I would have to deal with. This meant that I must get to
know the prisoner this evening, but at the same time must take
care not to let him find out prematurely the reason for my
presence. I was aware that I would have to employ strategy,
and even subterfuge, to attain this end; my reasons for doing
so, namely my wish to allow the condemned man a final, un-
troubled night on earth, seemed to me sufficient justification. I
hurried back, along the road that led to the command building. The wind, which had been blowing hard across the plains
all afternoon, had risen to gale force during the evening. The
semi-blacked-out hanging lanterns outside the prison gate
swayed back and forth and the gate itself, that led into the
courtyard, creaked on its hinges. I rang. I rang again. At last I
heard the footsteps of the guard.

"Who's there?"

I gave my name and rank.

"Password?"

Now I didn't know the password. I repeated my name and
rank, and added, "I've just arrived from Vinnitsa."

The sentry, a reliable, cautious man, thought for a moment
or two. Then he opened the gate and the harsh light of his
torch shone brightly in my face.

"I am the Protestant chaplain, and I should like to have a
word with Sergeant-major Mascher."

"Yes, sir."

I followed him into a deserted guardroom. There were two
tables, five chairs, a rifle rack, and the usual books—the guard
roster, the day report book and the punishment book. There
were identical rooms to be found in every part of Europe that
Hitler had conquered. The very air—with its mixed odors of
rifle oil, army cloth, cooking utensils and soldiery—was imme-

diately recognizable for what it was: the breath of the one
great prison that Europe had become.

The guards themselves were in a neighboring room, from
which came the so familiar sounds of a barrack room by night:
the banging down of playing cards, the mysterious numbers
shouted like pistol shots, "Seventeen!" "Twenty-four!"
"Twenty-seven!" punctuated by the sad, monotonous and
equally mysterious "Away!" Silence fell for a moment while
the sentry was delivering my message. Then I heard a hoarse
voice saying, "The holy Joe! Well, blow me down." There was
a short pause. "Must be on account of Baranowski. Tell him
I'll be right out."

"The sergeant-major will be right out, sir."

In order to say something, I asked, "Are you having a celebration this evening?"

The sentry replied, "No, sir. Dinner's at six, and that's really
the end of the day for us. Except for guard duty. Luckily
there's not much doing here."

The warrant officer appeared at this point, preceded by a
strong smell of vodka.

Only for a moment was I tempted to greet him with the
words: "The holy Joe is very sorry he has to interrupt your
card game." As soon as I saw him I felt sorry for him. He stood
there, so stolid and blue-eyed, and who knows? If I had been in
charge of Proskurov prison might not I, too, have taken to
vodka and skat as a means of escape?

"I'm sorry I must trouble you," I began. "As you know, Private Baranowski is to be executed at dawn tomorrow. I have
been sent here from Vinnitsa to prepare him for his end."

"Yes, chaplain sir."

"It is most important to me that I should get to know Baranowski, at least slightly, this evening. On the other hand, for
obvious reasons, I don't want him to guess why I'm here any
earlier than is absolutely necessary. It'll be time enough for
that tomorrow morning. I'd like to ask your advice about how
best this can be arranged."

The sergeant-major was doubtless unaware that he had unconsciously straightened up. Perhaps he realized that I actually
knew exactly what I wanted, and that my asking for his advice
was only politeness on my part. In any event, the glassy stare
had gone from his eyes when he replied.

"If I might make a suggestion to the chaplain, sir, Chaplain
Holze used to sometimes hold what he called barrack-room
meetings. You know the sort of thing, sir, a short service and a
friendly chat. Perhaps the chaplain would like to get the men
together for one now? Chaplain Holze held them once or twice
at night, so it wouldn't seem at all unusual. The men love it. It
helps them get through the long evening, you see. That way
you'd get an idea of what Baranowski's like. If you'll excuse
me saying so, sir, he's always struck me as a decent sort of lad.
I've always said it's a shame about the boy. But there you are.
Desertion's desertion. . . . Shall I tell my men to arrange it?"

"Yes, I think that would be a very good idea."

"We'll collect all the prisoners into one cell."

"Would there be room?"

"Oh, yes. There's one big communal cell. It's empty right
now. Besides, we've only got twelve prisoners inside at the moment."

"Good."

"Perhaps the chaplain would care to wait down here until
they're ready?"

"No. Take me to the cell and I'll wait for them there."

I had said this without thinking, and it was only while going
upstairs that I realized how advantageous it would be for me
to be in the cell before the arrival of the prisoners. Without
any questioning from me, which might have aroused suspicion,
each man, as he came in, would automatically say his name,
including the one man in whom I was interested. I assumed
that Baranowski would attend, though the service was volun-
tary. I imagined the sergeant-major to be right when he said
that almost all the prisoners came to the meetings, not just on
spiritual grounds but mainly because they provided a change.

Why should Baranowski stay away? Because, somehow, of his condemnation to death? I had learned by experience that condemned men do not believe in the reality of the sentence they have received; all that exists in the real world for them is the appeal they have sent off, those few lines of writing which they always compose and which are almost invariably fruitless. Well, I would see soon enough.

The man who had unlocked the cell door pulled a table out into the center of the room and arranged three benches in front of it. On the table I placed my cross, and the two candles which luckily I had kept in my pocket.

I heard the prisoners coming, their footsteps echoing hollowly in the night. It is strange how the soul can wander, how a single sound can summon up a whole segment of past life. Where had I heard such hollow footsteps before? I was of a sudden back in the monastery at Kloster Beuron, and the monks were walking down the corridors to the dark church for their evening service: *Almighty God, grant us a peaceful night and a holy end.*

They came in one by one. In the circumstances, the military stiffness with which they announced their names seemed grotesquely exaggerated; life itself would have to be shattered before that rigidity could be broken. I paid no attention to their names, since there was only one man here who interested me, but I examined each face with care. The man on whose account this had all been arranged was the last but one, and I thanked God that he had come. I looked for something remarkable in his features. He was the only one not to have a prison pallor; and in his bronzed face his slanting eyes were very sad, witnesses to the harshness of the life that had been his.

I wondered how best to arrange this meeting. I could start off with an evening service, followed by a few words with each man. Or alternatively it might be better to have a little general conversation, so that we could get to know one another, and finish by reading them a passage from the Bible.

I decided on a compromise. It seemed to me best to begin by asking each man to repeat his name and to tell me also where he came from and what his civilian profession had been. That is all neutral ground. For the moment I would not ask anything about their crimes or the punishment that they were undergoing, though perhaps later on it might be possible to have word with one or other of them on that score.

"Private Baranowski. Küstrin. No profession."

"I have a friend who comes from Küstrin. Pastor Lilienthal of the Ostkirche."

Baranowski looked up quickly as I said my friend's name, a mingled expression of incredulity and pleasure on his face. He said, "Yes? He confirmed me."

"Really? He's stationed near where I am at the moment. He's a private in a Landesschutz battalion."

"Pastor Lilienthal. I'd love to see him again. He was a wonderful man."

"Would you like me to give him any message from you, Baranowski?" (Careful now, I said to myself, as I asked this question.)

Baranowski's features relapsed into their previous expression of sadness.

"No, don't bother. It was seven years ago. He's sure to have forgotten me. There must have been so many others since then . . ."

"I doubt that. He has an incredible memory for names and faces and for people generally."

"No, I'd rather you didn't say anything about me to him."

I let it pass, and said the few words that I had prepared for the prisoners, using as my text the passage in Saint Luke's Acts of the Apostles: *And at midnight, Paul and Silas prayed, and sang praises unto God: and the prisoners heard them.* It needs great care in the choice of words to expound that message at any time and in any place, for there are many pitfalls. Here it was particularly difficult. I must avoid any falsity of tone or untrue stress. It was up to me to show them how and why at this special time and in their special predicament, the ability to sing the praises of God at midnight was a precious gift bestowed on them.

Finally we sang a hymn together, and then another; and after that it was easy for us to talk together. I sat down among them on one of the benches.

Now it must be understood that in those military prisons young boys were frequently to be found who in the remote civilian world would never under any conditions have seen the inside of a jail; their offenses were such as only a military code would ever have dreamed of punishing. Insubordination, for instance, often meant nothing more than that the poor fellow had lost control of his nerves. Although there were cases of stealing from a comrade, and that was a crime which nobody took lightly.

I asked a tall, thin young man, whose open, honest face had attracted me while I was preaching, why he was here. He seemed a good boy, and entirely unashamed, as he answered:

"Well, I picks up a girl and gets an infection and they ships me off to hospital. Talk about a cure! First-class, it was. The works. Only I couldn't stick them injections. Well, that was that. So I packs up my gear, cured you understand, and goes back to my mob and reports to the old man. And what do you know? 'Sentenced to three weeks close arrest for neglect of sanitary precautions and failure to report an infection.' So here I am, see."

This was no time for a sermon on morality. But I thought I might touch on another aspect of that problem.

"Which of you have children? Have you got any photographs of them with you?"

They soon had their wallets out and were passing the snapshots around. It was good to be there, beneath the oil lamp in the darkened prison. Baranowski, at whom I kept glancing unobtrusively, sat motionless as though enveloped in an invisible cloud. He had not taken out his wallet.

The turnkey entered.

"The chaplain is wanted on the telephone."

"Oh? What is it? Vinnitsa?"

"No. Third battalion Construction Regiment Five-three-two. Lieutenant Ernst."

"Very well. I'll come at once." And then, to the prisoners: "I'll be back directly, my friends, I want to have a closer look at those three little girls. I've got three like that of my own."

I hurried along the corridor to the guardroom. The field telephone lay on its side, off the hook.

"Hullo?"

"This is Lieutenant Ernst speaking. I should be very grateful if I could see you this evening. It's about the Baranowski business. I've been assigned to command the firing squad. I found out that you're at the prison now. Do you think when you've finished there you could spare me a few minutes?"

"Of course. With pleasure."

"Will you be there long?"

"No, I've about done for this evening."

"In that case suppose I were to meet you outside the prison in about ten minutes? Would that suit you?"

"Yes. Or if you'd rather, I'll come to your place."

"No, no. I'll walk along with you to your billets."

"Very well. In ten minutes then."

I replaced the receiver.

"I must just go upstairs again for a moment," I said to the sergeant-major who was coming through the door. In the big cell the prisoners were talking quietly together. I glanced once more at the Hanoverian's family group, and shook hands with them all. I did not say any of their names again, neither Baranowski's nor the others'. *A peaceful night and a holy end.* . . . They went back to their cells.

One of them turned back just before he left the cell.

"Thank you very much indeed," he said.

It was the young man who'd been sick. He spoke those few words, that are usually so banal and commonplace, with real feeling. And I thought again, as I had so often thought before, what a wicked, diabolical thing war is. Boys should be allowed to find their girls on the forest paths and taste their kisses fresh as fruit in a sunlit orchard.

Now I said good night to the men in the guardroom.

"I shall be back tomorrow morning, Herr Mascher, at four o'clock sharp. The legal officer has told me that he will be here at five-fifteen. I shall want to be alone with Baranowski for one hour."

"Very good, chaplain sir."

"Good night!"

"Good night, sir."

At the door I hesitated.

"What is the password for today?"

"Odessa."

"Password: Odessa."

[5]

"PADRE?"

"Yes, sir."

"I am Lieutenant Ernst."

"Good evening, Herr Ernst."

One of the compensations of my profession was that it enabled me to address most junior officers in this way, as though they were civilians. We didn't have any actual rank ourselves, but were treated as though we were roughly about the equivalent of majors; however, we really lived in a world of our own. Hitler regarded the chaplains' branch of the armed services as a superfluous appendix, which he frequently threatened to cut out. And, indeed, our organization as such was meaningless, though individual members of the branch were still capable of not inconsiderable achievements.

"I command a company in a construction battalion. We have been ordered by the Area Command to provide the firing squad, one and ten, for tomorrow morning, and I have been specifically put in command of that squad."

"A horrible assignment."

"I imagine that we are neither of us particularly happy about the parts we are being called on to play in this business. We are . . . colleagues."

"You mean that you . . ."

"Yes. I, too, am a pastor. In a village near Soest. I . . . excuse me, brother, but this assignment is beyond my strength. I can't do it."

He fell silent and we walked a little way without speaking. I could not see his face. I had only his voice by which to judge him, and it was a voice I liked. He might be from twelve to fifteen years older than myself, and so would belong to the generation which had taken part in the first war. He walked with a stoop, as though he had difficulty in holding himself erect. Now he stopped.

"I can't do it."

It sounded like the final pronouncement, the outcome of a long struggle. He spoke heavily, as though worn out.

"It's a trick, a foul, deliberate trick on the part of Major Kartuschke."

"Has the major something against you, then?"

Lieutenant Ernst took half a step toward me and, lowering his voice, replied, "We know each other, Kartuschke and I. At one time we knew each other very well indeed. To my regret, I must say. You see, twenty-two years ago, that is, back in nineteen-twenty, Kartuschke lived in my house for some months and was my vicar."

"But . . . but for heaven's sake. . . . You don't mean to tell me Kartuschke is ordained!"

So astounded and shocked was I that I almost shouted the words.

"Not so loud, brother, not so loud. The wind has ears. Yes, Kartuschke was ordained. Only for a short time, a year or so. It was a mistake, as he himself soon realized. He left the Church and embarked on a whole series of different careers. Or so I heard. I had lost all touch with him. Then, in thirty-three, when Hitler came, Kartuschke came back too. You remember how it was. The servants of the Church vanished; in their place came men sent to spy on the Church. It was an evil time. We sighed with relief two years later, when conscription was reintroduced and Kartuschke at last found an opportunity of becoming something. Now he's a major. And this means the end for me. But how could I have guessed that I would ever run across him in circumstances like these, that fate would give him the power to torment me?"

After a pause he went on.

"I tried, this afternoon, to get out of the assignment. Kartuschke was not in his office, or more likely he told his people to say he was out. I will not go to him begging for mercy. Oh, I can easily imagine the pleasure he's getting from doing this to me. You see, brother, I have three children. Do you have children too? You have? Then you understand the position I'm in. And I can't do it."

There was another pause. He asked, at last, "Have you nothing to say to me?"

"I simply cannot get over the fact that Kartuschke took the same ordination vows. . . ."

"My dear brother, forgive me for interrupting you, but let us forget Kartuschke for the moment. What are we to do? Am I tomorrow to give the fire order to the squad? By that time you will have prepared the prisoner for his death, and am I supposed to add the final touch to your work?"

"You put me in an extraordinarily difficult position, though it is in no way your fault. I should encourage you to obey the orders you have received tomorrow morning. I should attempt somehow to give you a clear conscience in which to carry out your foul task. What ought I to say to you? That if you refuse to do it, you will not be helping Baranowski the least little bit? It would make not the slightest difference to him, and the best that you could hope for would be that you would only lose your officer's commission. Would you be right to refuse? The result would be one less decent officer in this grim war, and one more inhuman one in his place. For replacements, as you well know, are easily found, they are cheap as dust. Or should you recall the words of Martin Luther who, four hundred years ago, had already asked himself whether men of war could be in a state of grace, and had answered himself that they could?"

"I see. Do evil in order to avoid greater evil, is that what you're getting at? The sword as the symbol of order. But what sort of order are we upholding with our war? The order of the graveyard. And the last cemetery, the biggest one of all, will be prepared for us. And if by some chance we should live through it and should be asked: 'What did you do?' then we survivors will all say with one accord: 'We bear no responsibility, for we only carried out the orders of others.' I can see it all already, brother, that vast army of men, each protesting his innocence, washing his hands of all guilt. They will need a huge towel on which to dry so many hands, a towel as large as a winding sheet. No, let us be serious. This is what I wish to ask you: are we in any way better than the Kartuschkes and their like? Or are we perhaps not even more corrupt than they? For we know what we are doing."

We had crossed the town square and entered a small park around which we had now walked twice. Ernst would stop from time to time, leaning forward and breathing in the night air, as though the damp October wind contained all that was left, in this place, of truth and decency and goodness. Suddenly he seemed to remember something else. He asked me, "Do you have a feeling for music?"

"I do indeed."

"Do you like *Fidelio*?"

"I love it. I cannot go into one of my prisons without recalling the aria 'to breathe in freedom.' "

"Yes, that's it: Germany and *Fidelio*, the Germany of nineteen-forty-two."

"My dear sir, *Fidelio* belongs to no one nation any more

than it belonged to the Viennese landowners of Beethoven's time. It belongs to the eternal spirit, and that spirit is a stranger on this earth."

"Yes, yes, but that's not the point. What I'm getting at is this: with that music ringing in our ears, we are prepared to perform our famous duty, carry out our celebrated responsibilities. You will do your job by giving him a sugar drop in the form of words of consolation, and I shall provide the less pleasant, though perhaps equally consoling, bullets."

"Brother Ernst, tomorrow morning at four I go to Baranowski's cell. I shall not take with me some sugar drop of consoling words, but, if I may, the bread and the wine of Christ. And that, as you know, is very different."

"Yes, I know. I know. Forgive me, put it down to the ghastly confusion in which I find myself if I talk rubbish. But tell me, tell me yourself: does it not cry out to heaven? Here are we, the servants of God, dressed in these foul clothes with the symbol of murder sewn above our hearts, hurrying through the dark streets of a Russian town, and tomorrow morning we are to shoot a boy dead. . . ."

The wind had now grown so fierce that I could not be sure whether that were the end of his sentence. I waited until we were walking between the houses again before I said, "You asked me earlier what distinguishes people like us from people like Kartuschke. Perhaps the difference lies in this, that we never, not even for a single hour, call evil good. It is true, bitterly true, that we are all ensnared in this witches' sabbath, that we are all guilty, every one of us. Nor is Baranowski guiltless; and had he been a British soldier, some English chaplain would have had to bear the guilt of accompanying him to his death. Our guilt is this, we live. And so we must live with our guilt. One day it will all be over, the war and Hitler will belong to the past, and then we shall have a task to tackle for which we shall need to be as honorable as we can be. What will then count will be our deepest personal feelings about this war and all its works. It will not be just a simple question of hating war. Hatred, one might say, is an active passion, and as such it must be exorcized. What must be done is to show people what a dirty business it has all been. Let the *Iliad* remain the *Iliad,* and the *Niebelungenlied* what it has always been, we must still show them that there is more nobility in rocking a cradle or wielding a pickaxe than in running after any Iron Cross. We must make them understand that war is sweat, that war is pus, that war is excrement. Day after tomorrow, and for a few years to come, everyone will know that. But just wait until a new decade has come, and you will see the old myths springing up again like weeds, like dragons' teeth. And we must be there, ready like good reapers to cut down that evil crop."

"Here is the Transit Billet. Thank you, dear brother. Give the young man eternal unction, and pray for my poor soul."

"For our poor souls."

"*Auf Wiedersehen.* We can hardly wish one another good night."

We shook hands and nodded. Lieutenant Ernst turned to go. I followed him with my eyes. He walked bent forward a little, as though he were carrying a great burden. Only then did I realize the implication of his farewell. He had decided to carry out the orders he had received.

[6]

MY FELLOW COUNTRYMAN HAD BEEN AS GOOD AS HIS WORD AND had lit the stove. The heat was delicious after the cold prison and the windy walk through the town. I took off my boots, put on a pair of comfortable slippers, and decided to make myself two cups of real coffee. The quartermaster had recently allotted me a small amount, "for emergencies." This, I thought to myself, could surely be counted an emergency. I had no trouble getting boiling water, for two Ukrainian girls were still at work in the kitchen; they were friendly and obliging, and with an amiable *dobre fetche* and *spassifo* I left them.

I had just sat down again, when there was a knock on the
door. The man from Balingen came in.

"I'm very sorry, chaplain sir, but I'm afraid I have to put
another officer in here for the night. He's a captain, flying to
the Eastern Front tomorrow morning."

"But of course."

I had scarcely time even to say these three words before the
man in question appeared in the doorway.

"Brentano," he said, and saluted. I told him my name and
held out my hand. He shook it in an easy, amiable fashion
before turning again to the soldier behind him.

"Please call me at six-thirty tomorrow."

"Yes, sir. Six-thirty, sir."

"When do you start serving coffee downstairs?"

"At a quarter to seven, captain sir."

"Good. That will just give me time. Thank you."

The soldier, now a model of military punctilio from head to
foot, saluted and went out. During the short interchange between them I had been struck by the quality of the young officer's voice, just as I had been, an hour before, by that of Ernst
during our windy walk together. This was a voice that kindled
friendship. Accustomed to command, yes, but then that was
inevitable. It nevertheless had retained a quality of lightness,
of delicacy. The air of authority was natural and in no way
underlined. There can be no question, the voice seemed to im-
ply, that what I command will be immediately and exactly
obeyed; therefore there is no sense in my wasting words, since
we both wish to make our relationship as easy as possible. I was
to discover that the voice was a perfect reflection of its owner.
He was to show me that that same war of which I had just said
such harsh things—and I had no intention of retracting a
single one of them—was all the same still capable of casting a
knightly shimmer, an Achillean glow. And this quality, I was
sure, was the flowering omen of future sacrifice: Captain Brentano would not come back.

"I must ask you to forgive my disturbing you. It is something
I do not like to do."

I looked at him, and as I did so it occurred to me that at no time had I managed to see Lieutenant Ernst's face. I should hardly recognize him tomorrow morning. We had walked together through the dark town, we talked and said things that were not unimportant to one another, and all this had happened without our seeing each other's features. I was glad that at least I knew what my second acquaintance of the evening looked like. Because of his name I found myself involuntarily searching for some resemblance to Clemens or to Bettina von Brentano in the young captain's reserved and serious face. There lay hidden fires, the gravity of death and the brilliance of life marvelously intertwined.

I replied, "Of course you are as entitled to this room as I am. There are no privileges. I suggest you take the bed in the alcove. I'll shade the light so that it doesn't shine in your eyes. You see I have some work that I must do tonight. I'm afraid it cannot be postponed."

Brentano had walked across to the window and began to busy himself with the black-out curtains, as though to cover some strange inner agitation. Then he came over to the table at which I was seated, and glanced at the still unopened file of documents before me. The Roman three on the cardboard cover was very plain to see.

"Roman three . . . and a pastor. That usually means something bad," he said.

"It means exactly what you have guessed it to mean."

"Look," he suddenly said loudly, as with an impetuous gesture he drew a piece of paper from his jacket pocket and placed it on top of the file. "You're interested in death sentences? There's no need to waste such a fat bundle of papers on one. A condemnation can be put very much more briefly. . . ."

I unfolded the single sheet of paper. It was a standard travel order, one of the many, many thousands that were made out during those years. We all knew them. This one ran as follows: Captain Brentano of the unit—there followed a pentagram—

was to proceed forthwith—and then, added in typescript "by air"—to the unit—and there came another pentagram—full stop—signed—Lieutenant-Colonel and Divisional Adjutant.

"Or it can be read this way. Captain Brentano is to fly to Stalingrad to join the Sixth Army. He will not be returning."

His voice was brittle as he said this. And he added, in almost the same tone, "No, I'm exaggerating. The odds are better than that. What sort of a chance would you say I have? I estimate it at about five in a hundred."

He turned back to the window. Clemens or Bettina? I asked myself once again. It was hard to say. Perhaps the nearest I could get to it was to recall some lines from Clemens' poem, "The Song of Fate": "I draw the bow, you aim the shaft, the arrow reaches to the heart." My attention wandered, as frequently happens when one is very moved, and my eye fell on Brentano's padded woollen jacket. It was not one of the standard army-issue greenish-gray jackets. It was almost white, of lamb's wool, hand-made, a token of personal love. I thought of the flocks of sheep on the distant island of Sylt, and their warm, silent existence.

"I must ask a favor of you," he began, and now the brittleness had all gone out of his voice. "I had, of course, no way of knowing with whom I should be sharing a room here tonight. To be exact, I had hoped that I might have a room to myself. Well, I haven't. Which is why I must ask this favor of you. It is one that I find particularly difficult to put to a parson. But I have no choice. And let me say that, judging from the little I have seen of you, it is far easier for me to ask you than I might have expected. To put it briefly, my fiancée, Sister Melanie, is downstairs. She has driven over from her hospital at Biala-Tserkov. I was able to send her a telegram letting her know that I'd be here for just twelve hours. Tomorrow morning I fly on to Stalingrad. We have nowhere to spend this last, restless night together except here. And we can only come here if you agree, if you will shelter us. I realize that this is an imposition, my friend, and that I . . ."

"Please do not think you have to worry about me in any way at all," I replied, interrupting him. "Of course you must be together here. Only I'm sorry, very sorry, that I cannot go elsewhere and leave you alone as you should be left. However, I can't. These documents, Herr Brentano, have to be read. And they have to be read tonight. The man they deal with will be laid in his wretched coffin at about six tomorrow morning. Before that I must talk with him. *Sub specie æternitatis.* It is an odd coincidence, but postponement is no more possible in his case than it is in yours. However, let me say that so far as you two are concerned I shall be here without being here. Ignore me completely."

Brentano walked across and shook my hand without a word.

"Sister Melanie is waiting outside in the storm?"

It was I who had broken the silence. Brentano now said, "I shall bring her at once. But first I must say this: I come of a family where life is hard. Or rather I should say a family that does not take life easy. When I left my home for the wars, my father's parting words to me were those of old Claudius: 'Never harm a girl, for remember that your mother, too, was once a girl.' I have thought a great deal about that, and indeed have done more than just think about it. But now . . ."

"Now, Herr Brentano, no. Now you must get Sister Melanie, and you must tell her that she has nothing to fear."

He went. I undid the bundle of documents dealing with Baranowski and opened it. At first I could see nothing save rubber stamps, marginal scribbles, signatures and rows of figures. My thoughts kept wandering. Perhaps I should try to help the lovers in some way. For some time now the house had been silent; but they could not be certain that they wouldn't meet some suspicious, prying person on the stairs or in the corridor. I went down and opened the back door; I had already explained to Brentano where the key was to be found. Then I saw the captain coming across the courtyard, and behind, with firm and measured steps, came a tall figure muffled in a long cape. With one of us on either side of the hooded girl, we went upstairs, taking care not to walk too fast, and Brentano and I even managed to exchange a few inconsequential remarks. Nobody saw us. While going along the corridor I thought I heard a light footfall behind us, but by then we had already reached the threshold of our room. We went in and I closed and bolted the door behind us. The unknown girl, still muffled to the eyes, stood by the table for a moment, as though to convince herself that all this was true; the chair, the table, her lover. Then she loosened her cape and turned toward me. She was radiant. But it is not enough simply to say that. Rather her whole person was concentrated in this one single quality. Embarrassment, shyness, anxiety, timidity, the certainty of parting and of death—all that was there too, but as it were engulfed, taken up and translated by her radiance.

"Just like Mozart's *Figaro*," I said with a smile, as I hung her cloak upon a nail. I added, by way of qualification: "If only it were all less serious." I had expressed myself badly, of course, but there are occasions when the wrong words can yet convey the right idea, can call up the correct emotions. So now, in the middle of that night, did I invoke divine music. Melanie laughed aloud and Brentano was encompassed in the laughter of Cherubino. The laughter of Cherubino? Cherubino doesn't laugh, he sings. Mozart sings on the edge of the abyss, in the very prescience of death.

"I have another cup of good coffee here, but nothing to offer it to you in."

"I have a canteen of black tea." Those were the first words that I had heard Melanie utter, and I thought how sweet her voice must sound to the sufferers at Biala-Tserkov, as she went among their beds urging them to sleep.

"I have wine," Brentano declared.

"A real banquet!" said Melanie. She had drawn up a chair, and opening her haversack took out cakes and white bread and honey which she shared among us.

"Shall I do it for you?" she asked, as she took his bread and spread the honey on it. We did not talk. Speech dies away on mountaintops and in the depths of chasms, and how far apart they are or how close only God can say, God and perhaps lovers. Thus is it, Brentano thought. And Melanie; thus might it have been, for a whole lifetime, always. And both of them: at least it will have been once. Or perhaps twice. And then once more, in Proskurov, in the night. And finally: it is forever.

"What shall we do about the light, Brentano?" I asked.

Sister Melanie had got up and was putting the packages back in her haversack. We had tacitly stopped addressing each other as "Herr," and had we had another half-hour together I believe we should have been calling one another by our Christian names, so strong was the magic of that hour and of our meal together.

"We must fix up your apartment, Sister Melanie, though I'm afraid our means are limited. You'd have done better to go to the Ritz."

Perhaps there is some law of nature by which, when circumstances are truly grave, only the lightest of manners is possible. The lovers could never have anticipated such a scene as this: that they would make their adieux, their wedding night beneath the very shadow of death, with a stranger only three paces away and with no dividing wall between him and them.

And now the three of us, who had just drunk together from the same cup, were suddenly separated as by a great gulf. They had their business to attend to, I mine. And my night's work, the study of Baranowski's folder, embraced a living creature no less truly than ever did a lover's arms.

[7]

THE DOCUMENTS WERE ARRANGED IN ORDER, IN CAREFUL CHRONO-logical sequence, with only this peculiarity: that the last document, the final word which was the dismissal of the appeal together with the order that the sentence be carried out, was on the top of the pile and therefore came first. And for a man reading alone at night this inversion was truly startling; thus, he might say, does a man's life appear when seen from its close, looking backward, and only the Almighty in His eternal wisdom is entitled so to observe a human existence.

Next came the prisoner's appeal, and, scrawled beneath it, the statement: "Forwarded without comment." It must have been the legal officer who had thus refused to comment. Neither yes nor no. In his heart he would doubtless sooner have scribbled a rapid "No," but he lacked sufficient determination even to do this.

There followed a copy of the death sentence: condemned for desertion and for the betrayal of military secrets. Under this were the papers dealing with the trial itself, a fairly numerous collection. I glanced through, noticing names. details here and there, signatures. I read: "B.'s correspondence," "Quartermaster Schildt," "the woman Liuba," and . . . and what was this? Another court-martial sentence? Yes, another one: "condemned to three years close arrest." By this time I was thoroughly confused. Apparently whatever it was that he had done and that was now to cost him his life was his second offense.

There was nothing for it but to start again and to go through all these papers in the correct chronological sequence. Being lacking in eternal wisdom, I could not read backward. The facts, I discovered, were as follows:

Fedor Baranowski was born on the nineteenth of November, nineteen hundred and twenty, in Küstrin, the illegitimate son of a shopgirl. His father was a Polish-speaking cabinetmaker of German nationality, a married man. There was no further information given about the father, who had apparently neither signed a recognition of paternity nor contributed anything toward the child's support. Shortly after Fedor's birth his mother had married a textile dealer by the name of Hoffmann; she, too, had apparently preserved only a vague connection with her son. The boy worked for a market gardener at one time, then he had a job with a second-hand dealer in Danzig, after which he returned to Küstrin. There seemed no question of his having had any sort of regular education, nor had he ever been apprenticed to any trade. When the war started Baranowski became a soldier. What most men associate with their childhood—meals at regular hours, a bed of one's own, fixed periods of sleep—Baranowski first learned to know in the barrack room. A barracks for a home. This fact, with all its obvious consequences, was clearly brought out by a statement in a generally most favorable character report on the man: "he receives no letters and no Christmas parcels." (The C.O. of the regiment, who had initialed this company commander's report, must have been an unusually conscientious man, for he had taken the trouble to write in the margin, beside this remark: "Uninteresting and irrelevant.") No less significant was the statement: "has nothing to do with women." This was in the report from the commander of his training unit. "B.," he had written, "is a quiet, well-behaved soldier, in no way outstanding. He lives moderately, has no apparent interests, and has nothing to do with women." There followed statements about his transfer to the front, his two wounds, the award of the Iron Cross second-class, his promotion to private first-class, and to lance-corporal; after his second wound (he was shot through the knee), he was sent to a rear area and transferred to a construction unit. Owing to his physical condition he was employed in the cookhouse, and it was there that his knowledge of Polish and Russian was first revealed. It was nowhere explained how he happened to speak those languages, but he had probably picked them up during his early years in Danzig. In any event, it was on account of this knowledge that the quartermaster of his unit took to sending Baranowski out from time to time to make purchases in the neighborhood. The unit was engaged in construction work of a very secret nature, and therefore, for security reasons, the soldiers had been particularly forbidden to fraternize with the natives. Unlike most

units, this one employed no Ukrainian men or girls, and there
were strict orders enforced about where the men might go on
the rare occasions when they were allowed out at all. Baranowski, however, in view of his linguistic abilities, was sent round
the neighboring villages to buy eggs and vegetables.

Now Liuba appeared in the story. There was little information given about this Ukrainian girl with whom he was to become so deeply involved, but what follows seems to have been
more or less what happened. Baranowski had come across
Liuba in one of the villages. She seems to have been a very
young widow, whose husband had died in the July battles,
leaving her with a child aged, at that time, about two. There
are reasons to believe that it was the child, rather than the
mother, that first began to play an important part in Baranowski's life. A child's smile to a soldier on active service is an oasis
in the desert, and it is easy to understand how he would have
wished to hold fast to this promise of life. Now, owing to the
nature of their construction work, his unit was frequently being moved from one place to another. Baranowski had taken to
informing Liuba of these moves, perhaps even through the
intermediary of a third party; in any event there were letters,
and those letters sufficed to condemn him. A party of S.S.
troops, raiding a village, got hold of a number of these little
notes of his to her, some of which were unluckily written on
the blank side of ration returns. Every unit carried blocks of
these forms, and it seems that Baranowski had been detailed to
look after them. As a result, the military police had no trouble
whatever in putting their hand on the culprit; as writer of the
notes he was soon under arrest, and there was nothing anyone
could do to avoid the consequences. The information he had
given was entirely harmless, but all the same he had informed
the Ukrainians of the movements of a Wehrmacht unit. In
brief, he was accused of "betraying military secrets," an offence
that carries a normal sentence of five years close arrest. As it
happened his punishment was milder, for he only got three
years. A number of officers who had known him had done their

best for Lance-corporal Baranowski, but such was the law that, in fact, they could really do almost nothing on his behalf.

The case was tried at Rovno, and at that time the chief military prison was at Dubno. He was to be sent there, whence he would almost certainly go to a penal company in one of the so-called Reformatory Battalions. The sentence itself, according to an order of Hitler's, would not be served until "after the war"; but to survive the war at all in a penal company a man needed an extremely capable and active guardian angel. . . . On the way to Dubno the prisoner succeeded in jumping out of the moving train. Miraculously enough he was almost completely unhurt, and owing to his knowledge of the language he was able to get help from the inhabitants. A change of clothing turned him into a Ukrainian civilian. Search parties were sent out after him, but without success. He had simply disappeared.

Three weeks later the following occurred. An area of forest that was supposed to contain partisans was cordoned off and combed by the military. A number of men, women and children who had been living in those woods were arrested, and among them was Baranowski. They were all marched off to a village in which, by a curious coincidence, Baranowski's old unit was stationed at the time. The partisans were standing, their hands above their heads, in the village square awaiting the arrival of the interpreters to interrogate them, when a sergeant from Baranowski's unit, hurrying by, happened to glance at the captives. He stopped, walked across, recognized his former cookhouse assistant, and cried out in astonishment, "What in God's name are you doing here, Baranowski?"

That was the end. What eventually happened to the people who had been rounded up (who, incidentally, did not include either Liuba or her child) I do not know. Baranowski was arrested at once and taken to Proskurov in irons. Here, on September 5, the second trial took place. It seems not to have taken long. The question of whether, in addition to his other crimes, he was also guilty of connivance with the enemy, was hardly raised; the facts of desertion were so indisputable that even the officer detailed to defend him could not bring himself to plead that the accused had only been "absent without leave."

I closed the bundle of documents and thought. So this was the external story of a man's life? What would the true story, the inner one, look like?

There could be little doubt that this was the history of a man who had been insufficiently loved. A man to whom life had denied even that modicum of warmth and affection without which normal development and growth are not possible. No letters, no parcels for Christmas. And then Liuba and the child. Not just any Ukrainian girl, but specifically this mother. "Has nothing to do with women," that was what they had said. And then this woman had come into his life. Liuba—he may have thought—whose husband our people shot, whose baby we made fatherless. And now I am here in that man's place, and here I shall remain.

I gazed in front of me. I felt as though I, too, had lived through those August weeks that the young man had passed deep in the woods, doubtless sharing a small hut with Liuba and the child. I could taste the dry warmth of the summer forest, I could smell the mushrooms and the wild berries, and I could see the man, become almost a Ukrainian himself by now, as he wandered through the clearings at first light or among the shadows of evening, hunting for food. He would glance quickly from side to side, alert, ready to run, always and at all times conscious of danger. He would breathe with relief when at last the door of the little hut closed behind him. Men would come to visit them from time to time; and why should Baranowski worry whether or not they were partisans? They would sit for an hour or so over the fire, roasting potatoes in its ashes, smoking coarse, black tobacco, talking in a dialect that the stranger could scarce understand. And then there were the nights, the stars among the treetops, the last flicker of the dying embers, the fires of love. Anxiety? Perhaps that, too, was always present, but also there was the voice of the loved girl and the soft breathing of the sleeping child.

A sudden sound awoke me from my reverie. Someone was

speaking my name. Where was I? In the forest night in August, listening to the heart-beats of happiness? No, I was in the Transit Billet at Proskurov, and it was Brentano's voice. He asked, whispering, "How late is it?"

I looked at my watch and whispered back, "One o'clock."

There was silence, and then a voice, that was not meant for my ears, but which I could not help hearing, said, "Six hours more."

And more softly, "Six moments more."

And then another voice—and it was wrong that I should have heard it. Forgive me!

"Six years more."

Such is the sweetness of love that its hours become as moments, and such its wisdom that its moments each fill a year. Yet this one night meant forever.

I did not stir. I looked through the documents again, but now I could no longer read such stuff. It was enough. Now I would consult something far above all documents.

And so I read:

For he doth not afflict willingly nor grieve the children of men. To crush under his feet all the prisoners of the earth, to turn aside the right of a man before the fact of the most High, to subvert a man in his cause, the Lord approveth not. Thou drewest near in the day that I called upon thee: thou saidst, Fear not. O Lord, thou hast pleaded the causes of my soul. . . .

I looked up, and saw Sister Melanie standing before me. She was wearing her cloak again, and in only one thing was she a different person from the one I had seen before. Her dark hair hung loose, and thus of a sudden she was no longer a nursing sister; she was just a girl, just a woman.

"The shutter keeps banging so," she said in a low voice. "Could we not fasten it?"

"I don't think so. There's such a storm blowing that I doubt if it would do any good. But I'll try."

I walked over to the window and opened it. The wind with black fury burst into the room, and I was glad that I had put the documents safely away. Melanie came over to the open window; her face, her whole being, were open and welcoming. Her future, as well she knew, was impenetrable. Yet the force of life lay in that future, and so she greeted it.

I had fastened the shutter back, and now I closed the window. Melanie turned away.

"He is asleep," she said, with a gesture toward the alcove. And I thought, This too is granted her, that she may watch over her beloved while he sleeps.

"You should try to get a little rest yourself, Sister Melanie."

"Oh, there's the whole winter for that."

"I'm going to switch off the light for an hour."

She gave me her hand. It was her silent farewell, and then she turned away.

A candle stood on a chair, and beside it my watch. I did not dare to make the room entirely dark, for I must not fall asleep. Sleep was forbidden to our generation: such was the war, Hitler's war. In whatever hell he now floats, the spirits should constantly shout that in his ears: you stole our sleep, you stole our sleep, you stole our sleep and our children's sleep. I thought of brothers, of friends, of our dearest people, all listening in the night, with weariness lying heavy on their eyelids, and yet they dare not sleep. Occasionally one about to depart would be so overwhelmed by his exhaustion that he would sink into a deep, deep silence. And Baranowski too, I thought, would sleep calmly. Storm, you wild, night storm, you raging, shouting window-rattler, rave at me as you will! But do not waken those who are dedicated to death.

And now it was half-past three. I pressed a damp sponge to my eyes and forehead, forcing somnolence away. Everything that had to be prepared was ready. There were only the documents, and I tied them up again carefully with their piece of string. And while knotting it I realized, with the sudden shock of such awareness, that I was the last person on earth who would ever read through that bundle of papers. In two hours time, when the clock had struck, no human soul would ever again wonder about this man's story. But in the lamentations of Jeremiah it is written: *O Lord, Thou hast pleaded the cause of my soul.* And that was written for Baranowski, too.

I crept quietly downstairs. The storm had become so huge and violent that I could barely manage to force open the front door. I struggled from street corner to street corner, as though I were fighting to capture this town from some fanatical defender.

[8]

"PASSWORD?"

"Odessa."

The sentry unlocked the gate. In the guardroom stood Sergeant-major Mascher. He was dressed in field-service uniform, and he gave me a smart salute. His manner was very different from that of the night before. A freshly lit fire crackled merrily in the grate, but we shivered nonetheless. How could we help it? The proximity of death is a cold wind to the living. All the same, I was beginning to undo my overcoat when Mascher said, "It's cold up there."

"I can't help that. If I went in with my overcoat on it would look as though I didn't intend to stay with him."

"Shall we go up then?"

As we walked along the corridor the sergeant-major asked me, "Will the chaplain tell him, sir?"

On either side of us lay the cells. He spoke in a low voice; everything was to be done as quietly as possible so that the other prisoners should not know what was happening. Yet they would know; that was certain. Not only tomorrow morning, when Baranowski did not come to work (for perhaps he had not gone out to work, perhaps they had kept him in his cell the whole time). No, they would be aware of it tonight. Death has the power to creep through crannies like a fever, and it can slip into sleeping men's dreams.

"Will the chaplain tell him, sir?"

I was not bound to do so. The actual announcement was a matter for the military. Yet must I not respect this good soldier's awe, his reluctance and his natural agitation?

"Yes, I'll tell him." (But how? I asked myself. How?)

The guard unlocked the cell door and stepped back.

"I'll go in first," said the sergeant-major.

He switched on his pocket torch and its beam caught the sleeping man. Only the top of his head was visible, for his cell was indeed cold and he had wrapped his blankets tightly around him, a living creature with a creature's love of warmth. He did not move.

The sergeant-major shook him.

"Get up, Baranowski!"

Yet he spoke with a sort of gentleness. In the barrack room his voice would have been very different.

Baranowski sat up, shielding his eyes for a moment against the torch's ray. Then he recognized the sergeant-major and, trained to obey, immediately jumped off the bed. I was standing in shadow by the door and he did not notice me.

"Get dressed. There's somebody here to see you."

"What is it? What's happening?"

"Don't ask questions. Hurry up."

He reached for his trousers and put them on. Then, with averted face, "Please, just one moment . . ."

The sergeant-major glanced in my direction and I stepped out into the corridor again where the guard was waiting. Baranowski went over to the bucket.

On such a morning as this one is acutely sensitive, perhaps overly so; still, in a tiny fissure a man may grasp the whole depth of the abyss. So now this stammered request for a moment's privacy seemed to me to contain within itself all creation's shame and abandonment.

"Hurry up now," I heard the sergeant-major say. "Get your bedding squared away."

Then he took a step toward the door and called to me.

"He's ready now, chaplain sir."

The door closed behind me. Baranowski stared at me with bewildered incredulity. He even forgot to salute.

"Can you guess what it is that brings me to your cell at such an early hour?"

"Is it because of the death sentence?"

"Yes."

"Has my appeal been turned down?"

"Yes."

"When . . . when will it happen?"

"Today."

"Today . . . ? When?"

"In one hour's time."

"Where?"

"Here, outside the town."

"Will I be beheaded?"

"Of course not, Baranowski. You're a soldier."

"A bullet then?"

"Yes."

"O God . . . and the appeal has been turned down."

There was silence. I took the cell's only chair and pulled the table around so that Baranowski would be on the far side of it if he sat on his bunk. The candle's light reached only a little way into the room. I opened my cigarette case, which I offered to Baranowski, and I took one myself. I handed him the candle to light his from. How wonderful it is to smoke! It is something to do at moments when inactivity would be literally intolerable. "You wanted to be a human being, if only for a couple of weeks; and now you must pay."

Such was the cue, or rather the theme. It was both superscription and summary.

"I did nothing wrong, padre sir."

Then, taking a long pull at his cigarette, "But I won't let them send me to a penal company, I won't."

It was as though he had not understood that in one hour's time no company in this world would ever trouble him again.

"There was a couple of men in our unit who told us about

the penal companies. Just a little bit of bread and cabbage soup, and they work you from four-thirty in the morning to seven at night, and they have N.C.O.'s who make you do everything on the double. Seems a fellow hasn't much hope of lasting long in one of them."

He didn't exaggerate. I had heard enough about them to know what a penal company in the year nineteen forty-two meant. So that was it: fear of a slow death had brought him here, had driven him straight to a quick death at o-five-forty-five hours behind the brickworks. And there I sat, I who was to share his last hour, who should hold with him his final conversation. We were on the very edge of life, and it was up to me that our talk should be a fitting one. I must allow him full freedom to say everything he wished, and yet I must remain in control. The subject of our talk was a double one: death and eternity. Death is freedom, but eternity is bondage: departure is grief, arrival is joy.

It was a severe task that lay ahead of me—it was as though I had to perform a grave and spiritual saraband. There were words to be spoken, comprehensible human words, but clearly there was more than just this. Klaus, my *frater catholicus,* could give absolution, the host and the chrism; he had for his people a language of signs which at one and the same time may not be understood and yet which must be and is understood. But I, here, today? Up there, in my own district, I knew the men condemned to die in the prisons as well as, and frequently much better than, the other men condemned to another sort of death in the hospitals. We had a broad basis on which to build our last hour together, and there was never need to try to start at the last moment. Here I must begin from almost nothing. For, strictly speaking, I should not admit that I knew what I had read in the documents. Otherwise he might well say to himself that the pastor had been spying on him, and had come here with the intention of putting something across. I could imagine him saying: "No thanks. No rubbish for me from your pious junk shop."

"We have one hour left to spend together. It is up to us, my friend, to make the most of it."

Was that the right way to start? I had said it principally to myself.

"Is there anything you'd like me to do for you? Perhaps we could write a letter together? A letter to somebody you love and to whom you would like to send a message."

He didn't answer at once. Then he said, "No, thank you. There's no one."

Now it was time for me to put aside all subtleties and subterfuges and tell the truth.

"I read part of the documents connected with your case, Baranowski. I had to, you see."

"Then you know all about it."

"I do. But you can never tell from such documents whether the picture you are getting is the true one or not."

"Well . . . it doesn't make any difference . . . any more."

"Quite. I was only wondering. Wouldn't you like to send a word to . . . to Liuba?"

Baranowski looked up at me now. To hear Liuba's name in this place, in this cell. . . . But he glanced quickly away, his eyes settling at last on the flame of the candle.

"There'd be no point in writing to her. The letter would never get there."

"It would."

"How?"

"I'll make it my business to see that it does."

"You?"

"Yes, me."

(It was forbidden. Of course it was forbidden. It was forbidden even to be human. But this was the desire, the last testament of a dying man. The devil take the war and all its regulations.)

"Have we got time enough?"

"Yes, plenty of time."

"Have you got writing paper with you, padre sir?"

"Here."

He took the sheets and placed them neatly in front of him. Suddenly a fierce spasm shook him. He could not stop trembling.

"Shall I write it for you?"

"That would be kind of you. Do you know Russian?"

"No, but I do know the letters. I can write the cyrillic alphabet. You'll have to dictate to me very slowly."

"Then you won't know what you're writing for me."

"It concerns nobody but you two."

He dictated and I wrote. I could understand a single word here and there. They were human words. This was no betrayal of military secrets.

"Good. Now you must sign it yourself, or else Liuba will have no proof that the letter comes from you."

He wrote. His hand shook violently, but at last he managed to make his signature.

I noted the name of the village, and he told me how to find her house. I put the letter away in the inside pocket of my wallet. And that was that.

"Should I not tell Pastor Lilienthal about our meeting one another?"

"Give him a greeting from me, if you like. But I don't think it'll mean much to him."

"Do you still remember the catechism that Pastor Lilienthal taught you?"

"No. I've forgotten it."

"Don't you remember any part of it, even roughly? If you can recall it at all we might repeat it together."

"Well . . . there was something about drinking in it, I think."

"That's right. 'If any man thirst, let him come unto me and drink.' "

"Yes, that was about it. I should tell you I've never bothered much with religion and church and all that. But I've always remembered a few bits of prayers. And these last few days

I've been thinking—about how it's all over and done with, and how there's no way of making anything any different now. I mean, I'd have to start again from the beginning, wouldn't I, if I wanted to change anything. Well, there's nothing we can do about that here, is there?"

He spoke rapidly, and he had dropped the correct, military High German in favor of his Pomeranian dialect, and this made him seem suddenly like a boy again. An anxious furrow in his brow had been as though stroked away, and in his eyes, which had been vacant, there was now life, life and fear.

"You are wrong," I said. "It has everything to do with us here."

What should I say to him? That eternal love does not refuse him whom this world thrusts out? That we are all incalculably sinful, and that yet the peace of heaven is offered to every one of us? And that, though we may not be invited to the banquets of life, the last table is still laid ready and waiting?

I cleared the cigarette ash away, and spread a white cloth over the table. On it I placed the cross, the host and the chalice. I spoke the words of the general confession and pronounced absolution. They were the same words that I had spoken so often in my village at Easter, and in the hospital by so many deathbeds. When I came to the Lord's Prayer he joined in, slowly and awkwardly. But the words were out now, those great sentinels of eternity. No sound came from without to disturb us. And even when a clock suddenly struck five somewhere, and I realized that the man with me would not hear that clock strike six, even then the feeling of security did not leave us.

The celebration was over. We sat down again.

Baranowski asked, "Have we any time left?"

"Yes. Why?"

"I could . . . because of what you said about peace . . . I'd like to write another letter."

"To whom?" Though I had already guessed.

"To . . . to Frau Hoffmann."

"Yes. Let us write it together."

I wrote while he dictated.

"I must tell you . . . no . . . I'm sorry to have to tell you that I am going to be shot at dawn today. The pastor is with me now. He will write you about it. Thank you for all you did for me. I'm sorry it's finishing this way. Think of your son sometimes . . ."

And he signed again. Fedor.

"And the salutation, my friend? Every letter must begin with a person's name."

He hesitated. Then he wrote: Dear Mother.

"Now be calm. I shall go with you. I shall stay with you till the end."

"Till the end," he repeated. "Will it be quick? Will they kill me with the first shot?"

"They will."

His eyes wandered around the cell. (Now, I thought, the time is ripe for the legal officer to come.) Then he pulled out his wallet which contained the few private possessions that they had allowed him to keep. Among them were two photographs.

"That's her," he said.

It was Liuba, a Russian snapshot that was certainly no masterpiece. But her face, so far as one could see it, was a face for which a man would risk much, very much.

"You'll see her. And that's the boy. A fine kid."

He tore up the photographs.

It was at this moment, as he tore the snapshots across, that he cut himself off irrevocably from the love and warmth of life. And now he suddenly stood up. Turning toward me, he gripped me by both shoulders. Then, almost timidly, he slipped his arms around my neck and kissed me on the mouth, saying, "Thank you, thank you, thank you."

And he seized my hands, and whispered, "What good warm hands you have."

He was a different man from the soldier I had seen the night before in the communal cell with the other prisoners. He had quickly recovered a fragment of life; this last hour had not been barren.

"Your letter will be delivered. You can be sure of that."

This was all that I had time to say, for I heard footsteps coming down the corridor. We stepped apart and stood at arm's length; the emotion of parting, which had made brothers of us, was not for the eyes of strangers.

The door opened, and two members of the field police, the so-called bulldogs, came in, each with a machine pistol in his hand. Immediately behind them was the legal officer, now wearing a steel helmet. He saluted me sharply and turned to Baranowski. The prisoner was standing rigidly at attention, expressionless, beside his bunk.

"Fedor Baranowski! It is my duty to inform you that the General Officer Commander-in-Chief Ukraine has decided as follows: the appeal of Private Baranowski is dismissed and the sentence passed is to be carried out. In accordance with this order you will be shot today. Remember that you are a soldier! Behave accordingly!"

He left the room at once. Baranowski did not move. The bulldogs came across and handcuffed him. Not a word was said. One of the prison guards, a pleasant-looking boy, entered the room with a pocket knife in his hand. According to standing orders, he proceeded to cut off the prisoner's shoulder tabs, the national emblem on his left breast, and his medal ribbons; the two lance-corporal's stars had already been taken away at the time of his loss of rank. He had difficulty in cutting away the national emblem, for the threads were tough and would not break. Nobody had much patience left. The soldier ripped at it, and a piece of the cloth came away.

"Mind what you're doing," growled one of the field policemen.

"I've almost finished," said the guard, in a strong Bavarian accent, and that accent struck a soft, sad note in the harshness of the dawn.

The field policeman's voice was very different.

"I warn you that at any attempt to escape I shall use my pistol immediately."

Fedor Baranowski did not reply. His eyes were still far away, but his rigidity no longer reached down to his heart.

[9]

THERE WAS A FINAL SCENE IN THE GUARDROOM.

"Where do you want your effects sent? Have you left an address?"

I answered for him.

"I have the address."

"Would you like a cup of coffee?"

Baranowski nodded. "Yes, please."

The sergeant-major said, "Take the handcuffs off of him."

The field policeman replied, "It's against regulations." But, after a moment, he added, "Still, I guess he won't try any tricks on us."

The handcuffs were unlocked and the condemned man took two or three sips of coffee.

"How about a slice of bread?"

"No, thanks."

"Another cigarette?"

Of a sudden they were all anxious to do what they could for him. By the offer of such alms do we attempt to cancel the guilt that is in our lives.

A car stopped outside. A member of the escort came into the room, and said quickly:

"Come on, let's go."

Baranowski was quite calm by this time. He laid down his half-smoked cigarette in the ashtray, shook hands all around like a man starting off on a long journey, and finally, while the handcuffs were being snapped on again, asked me, "Will you be coming with me, chaplain sir?"

"Yes, I'll stay with you."

It was the hour between dawn and daylight. The wild storm had dropped. A moist and gentle west wind blew in our faces.

In the courtyard a transport sergeant was standing, giving instructions for the move off.

"You and the man in there," I heard him say to one of the field policemen. Then I caught the voice of another soldier, a member of the escort, murmuring, "That won't do, sarge . . . The coffin's in that one."

"Would the chaplain care to drive with the legal officer in the small car up there?"

"No, I'm staying with Baranowski."

"Very well, sir. There's room for four in the truck up front."

So there we sat, the field policemen, Baranowski and I, and the drive began. The legal officer's car had already set off. The field policemen, relieved that there had so far been no hitch in the proceedings, leaned back and did their best, according to their lights, to cheer up the prisoner.

"Damned silly," said one.

And the other, "Keep your pecker up. We've all got to go some time, that's what I always say."

I was beginning to feel the effects of my sleepless night. Half annoyed as I was, I yet couldn't help being amused by this "pecker up." Meanwhile we drove on, meeting nobody and nothing on the road, for which I was glad. For a while we followed the road by which I had come to Proskurov the day before; and then the car turned off to the left, along a cart track over which we bumped and swayed, for it was really no road at all. Suddenly we saw ahead of us all the dreary festivity of military pomp; gray steel helmets and brilliantly polished belt buckles glistened in the morning light. To the left a company of infantry was drawn up; in the middle stood the execution squad; and on the right a few officers were grouped about the wooden post. The truck stopped and we got out. Baranowski, who had not spoken a single word during the drive out, walked slowly over to the post. He stood there and was blindfolded.

The legal officer now began to speak. The regulations laid down that he must once again recite the verdict of the court-martial and the confirmatory judgment. It was a pitilessly long speech. His voice today sounded exactly as it had when I heard it yesterday; utterly impartial, utterly emotionless.

I had joined the group of officers but without looking at them. I was shocked suddenly to hear Kartuschke's voice, sharp as a knife in the morning air, and it was with a start that I realized it was me he was addressing, as he said loudly, "The army chaplain!"

I knew a hundred pairs of eyes were watching me, but I was conscious only of one pair, and they could not see me for they were covered by the white blindfold. I walked over to Bara-nowski. Standing close to him, and in a voice so low that only he could hear, I said, "Think only on this: *Into Thy keeping my spirit I commit; for Thou hast redeemed me, Lord, God of love and truth.*"

He said, "Would you give me your hand once more?"

Awkwardly, for he had not the blind man's sense of touch, he reached for my hand. I gave it him, calmly and firmly. It was good. I was there as a servant of the Gospel, and thus did I show what the place of us servants is: we are with those who fall beneath the harrow. The truth of the Gospel is folly to the world, its scorn and anger. So it was that morning, as I stood there with his hand in mine. Then I stepped back. I had walked halfway across when the shots rang out. Lieutenant Ernst had given the fire order silently, by means of a gesture.

Baranowski had fallen on his face. The staff doctor, a small, thin man whom I now noticed for the first time (he did not look as though he were enjoying his early morning duties) stepped across to the post, felt Baranowski's pulse, examined his eyes, drew out his watch, faced about, and reported to Kar-tuschke in a cracked voice, "Dead at o-five-five-seven hours."

The unpainted coffin was lifted up and brought across, but first two soldiers drew off the dead man's boots, for the Wehr-macht was short of leather. Men of the escort placed him in the coffin, and on the sandy ground where he had lain there was now a pool of blood. Nails and hammers were ready. Everything had been prepared, for the German army was a thorough organization, and it had a drill for all eventualities, even for executions by shooting.

Meanwhile the commanders of the various bodies of troops were marching their men off, and I had rejoined the group of officers, whom I saluted without looking at them.

Over on the far side Lieutenant Ernst and his men were marching away. He walked heavily, bent forward a little even now. I had not managed to have a look at his face, and I regretted this. I would write him a note, tomorrow.

The legal officer came up to me.

"Shall I drive you back to town in my car?"

My immediate reaction was to decline, but I noticed that he had dismissed his orderly and was planning to drive himself. So presumably he wished to be alone with me for a few minutes. I could not refuse him his request.

"You handled it extremely well," said the legal officer as we drove off. I looked at him. He seemed to have absolutely no idea of what he was saying. He was simply trying to be agreeable. Frankly, I didn't know what to reply.

"It's cold," he went on, turning up his coat collar and settling himself more comfortably into the driving seat. He fumbled in his pocket for his cigarettes. Now I must say something.

"We both feel uncomfortable just now," I said. And I added: "And it is right that we should feel uncomfortable."

"What do you mean?"

"Justice."

He looked at me. His lighter had finally worked at the tenth attempt. He had just taken the first puff at his cigarette, and now, with sudden violence, he forced open the window. He took a deep breath of autumn air and said loudly, "Nuts!"

Then, after a pause, "Thank God I've still got some decent vodka back at my place. My reserve bottle. To be drunk sparingly. For special occasions. Firing-squad schnapps my orderly calls it. I'll invite you to join me in a drop, padre."

"Thank you, but it's no good."

"What do you mean? Moral scruples? How long have you been in this racket?"

"Three years."

"Three years and still uncorrupted. You must come straight from heaven. First-class."

"You mean because of my refusing your vodka? Normally I enjoy a glass. It is just that after what we have just seen I am not in the mood for it. You see, it was all a perversion of justice."

"What do you mean, a perversion? I didn't want a war. But since we've got one we'd better make the best of it. One way or the other, as Adolf keeps saying. Car or coffin. I'll take the car, thank you very much."

We drove a little way in silence. I realized that this man, who yesterday had spoken so firmly and coolly, was now stumbling over his words like a man clambering among ruins. Speech comes from God and exacts a true justice.

"I think I'll take a short stroll in the country," I said. "If you'd be so good as to drop me off."

"Very well, here you are. And God be with you. Once again, many thanks for what you did this morning. You certainly know your job."

"The best of luck to you."

[10]

ON THE OTHER SIDE OF THE ROAD A NARROW TRACK LED UP toward the high ground which I noticed on my arrival the day before. I was happy to be alone once again, and to be able to stride out once more (could it be only yesterday?) in the freshness of the early morning countryside. The events, the sequence of events, of the night before still held me; and when a military cemetery came in view on the high ground, it seemed a most fitting climax. So here Baranowski, too, would find his plot; not among the rows of other soldiers, certainly not with them, but away over to one side. And there, too, was peace. Let him rest in peace. No one would speak the words over his grave, so I would say them now, and they would retain their meaning, even if in three or four years another cataclysm should pass this way and turn this country into a wilderness. For that new tragedy could not be long delayed. The Soviets would regain their lands and their towns, and then no cross would stand in this cemetery, for crosses make good kindling for the fires of the Red Army. But Fedor Baranowski will have no cross, and so he will have none to lose.

A loud noise startled me. It was an airplane, flying low over the high ground. The pilot looked out and waved to me. I realized that the airfield must be very close.

I would make my way there; for it seemed a good place to go to now. I had no wish to return to the Transit Officers' Billet, though I was sure that the lovers would have departed. Sister Melanie must have left very early. Brentano would have accompanied her a little way before turning back. The soldier from Balingen would have knocked on his door at six-thirty, and now he would be eating his breakfast. Perhaps I might see him again at the airport.

The security precautions at the field were not strict, and my paybook was sufficient identification to let me through. There were a number of small planes getting ready to take off; the ground crews hurried hither and thither; and there was a general air of cheerful activity which this arm of the service managed to perserve from the very beginning even into the fourth year of the war.

"Good morning, chaplain!"

The voice came from behind me. Turning round I saw the station commander from Vinnitsa, a lieutenant-colonel with whom my duties had frequently brought me in contact. This flyer was what one might call a noble savage. We had discovered a mutual love of music, and an equally mutual hatred for Hitler and all his people. It was a constant matter of amazement to me how he—who was far more involved with the powers that be than ever I was—had managed to create about himself this un-fascist, human atmosphere which he liked to call his "warm front." Even this "good morning" was risky enough.

"What are you up to here?" he asked.

"I came down on duty, colonel."

"Somebody bit the dust?"

"Rather the other way round."

"Oh, I see." He understood at once. Our lives had become so primitive that we had learned quickly to grasp the few things that still existed. "This gang . . . Well . . . another item on the general account."

"Quite. Unfortunately, though, it won't bring those people back to life." And I gestured toward the cemetery.

"True enough, unfortunately. Meanwhile where are you off to now?"

"Back to Vinnitsa."

"Have you a car?"

"No. I must go to the transport office and get one."

"Nonsense. Fly with me. I'm leaving in an hour's time."

"I'd like to very much, colonel, only my stuff's at the Transit Billet."

"Good. We'll pick it up right away. I'll rustle us up a car and we can drive into town together."

We did so. The lieutenant-colonel had some business to transact at the headquarters building. It was on the tip of my tongue to tell him about Kartuschke, but I decided not to. Hadn't it all gone far enough already? Brentano's handshake, Melanie's laugh, the prisoner's kiss: all that I had. Also it suddenly struck me that what I was hating was not so much the evilness of the man as my own inability to cope with what I could not redeem. If that were so, I would do better to keep my mouth shut about Kartuschke.

The lieutenant-colonel dropped me off at the Transit Billet.

"See you in half an hour at the headquarters building."

"Right."

I went in through the back door, climbed the stairs without meeting anyone, and hurried along the corridor. I stopped outside the door and listened for a moment. There was no sound to be heard. I opened the door and went in. The room was empty; it was just a room like any other. No echo of the past night remained behind to say that this had been a place of love and vigil. There were no signs of past fears or happiness. I locked the door and handed back the key. In the breakfast room a few officers were still seated at the coffee table. Captain Brentano was not among them, and I did not ask after him. I did, however, leave a message for my friendly acquaintance from Balingen, since he was not about.

The lieutenant-colonel appeared through the door as I was nearing the headquarters building.

"Evviva il pastore!"

He loved foreign languages in general, and the Italian language in particular. An engineer by profession, he had traveled widely. What he enjoyed about his present work in the air force was the fascination of observing technical progress. But no new inventions, no matter how exciting, could prevent him from seeing beyond his airplanes. In the evenings he would play Vivaldi on the piano, occasionally interrupting himself in order to recite some poem from memory, usually one in a Romance language.

"I'm illogical, *signore*," he would say, "but try though I may I can't really bring myself to hate the *torre di Roma*. After all, he . . . well, he does speak the language of Dante."

"Avanti!" he now shouted, and back we drove to the airport as fast as we had come.

While we had been in the town a big plane had come in. Even as the prison guardroom had changed in a few hours from being a center of life to an anteroom of death, so now the atmosphere of the airfield was quite different from what it had been. The ground crews were apparently performing exactly the same tasks as before: officers stood in doorways smoking one cigarette after the other; pilots in their leather flying suits hurried across the grass with their flight orders in their hands. Yet it was as though a slate-colored, deathly seriousness had descended on the whole scene.

There stood the great machine, a JU 52, and seeing how solid and safe it looked, I understood why they often referred to these planes as "good old auntie Ju's." But this one was different: this was the Stalingrad plane, and in it Captain Brentano was flying to his death.

I had no way of knowing this, yet I was sure of it. The lieutenant-colonel seemed suddenly in a hurry. He handed over the car with scarcely a word to one of the airfield drivers and walked quickly across to the ramp. A strange pilot stood there, talking to two men. I hung back a little, but I heard what was said.

"Where are you flying to?" the lieutenant-colonel asked.

"To Rostov first, sir."

"And then?"

The pilot hesitated. His destination was obviously secret.

"All right . . ." the lieutenant-colonel immediately said, not wishing to encourage the pilot to disobey his orders. And he added, speaking softly, "Have you got any chocolate?"

For a moment the pilot looked at him with a puzzled expression; what on earth was the meaning of this question?

The lieutenant-colonel put his hand in his overcoat pocket and took out two bars of chocolate, which he gave to the pilot.

"*Hals-und Beinbruch!*"[1] he said, holding out his hand. That was quite a common flyers' farewell: they thought to banish the bad luck by naming it.

As for the handshake, the pilot knew well enough what that meant. He walked over to his plane and did not look back.

The lieutenant-colonel came over to where I was standing. I had never seen his face so gray. He said, in English, "Nevermore!"

Then, in a different tone, he went on, "I'll be right back and we'll take off at once."

I remained on the ramp, looking down over the field. The

[1] Literally: Broken legs and a broken neck.

pilot of the JU 52 had climbed aboard and the propellers were
beginning to turn. It was at this moment that I saw Captain
Brentano. He must have been standing on the far side of the
plane for some time; doubtless he wished to feel the earth of
Proskurov beneath his feet for as long as possible.

Now he came round toward the steps that led up into the
body of the plane. He glanced toward me. For a moment he
was not certain, and then he recognized me. I thought he was
going to run across and speak to me, but there was a shout
from inside the plane, presumably telling him that he was too
late. So he stopped and saluted me from the steps. And in that
gesture I recognized again the amalgam of qualities that Captain Brentano represented for me: military correctness and
ease of manner, the light of morning in the shadow of death.
Soon he was to be freed from all wars and all confusion—such
was the meaning of his salute to me. At some other time the
stiffness of his farewell gesture might have seemed to me
strange and antipathetic; but now I realized that this rigid
flick of his wrist was the only way he could still tell me what his
lips could not say: Melanie and death, a night of love and
nevermore. I saluted back. I could not have done it more
smartly had a field marshal been passing by. The door closed
and the airplane took off.

The lieutenant-colonel came back, wearing the light suit of
overalls that they used for short hops. He watched in silence
while the great bird disappeared.

"My crate's over the other side. Come on, we're off."

He gave me a few brief instructions, showed me the para-
chute and the safety belt and how the ripcord worked—"just
in case"—and then climbed up into the pilot's seat. It was a
two-seater plane of the dive-bomber type, and the observer sat
alone in a glass observation turret. Since there was nothing to
observe, I had the observer's seat.

Proskurov was soon out of sight, the commandant's office
building and the brickworks and, last of all, the cemetery. We
were already flying high and fast. Beneath us the land lay
stretched out, dark brown, broad and clear.

We had not gone far before we saw the storm again, that same storm which had beaten at the earth all night, and which, with the dawn, seemed to have withdrawn up here on high. I remembered the tales I had heard of the old Catalan battle-fields; were the ghosts of the fallen pursuing their battles up here, high in the sky? Down there—where I came from and whither I was bound—how much longer would the cruel indecision last? How long would the Kartuschkes rule? The guilty and the guiltless die, while the anxious wait, apprehensive till the day itself.

I had struggled successfully against my weariness long enough. Now it might overwhelm me. Perhaps our earthly laws do not apply up among the clouds. In any case, the train of thought that I had so obediently heeded and followed through the long night began slowly to fade away, and only dreamy fragments of imagination stayed with me.

What sort of face was it that I seemed to see, watching me from that cloud? It was a human face, a child's face, silvery white in its vague outlines. Could it be Liuba's son? I would find them both, the mother and the son, and perhaps I would give them the ring that had caught my eye the other day in the bazaar, the delicate ring with the two red stones. Two fathers, my son, have watched over you, and both are gone, and that you must not forget. But already the cloud is changing. It is no longer a single face, but has become a ring of faces, a swarm of *putti* such as Rubens loved to paint. So will the children be grouped together, far away in Soest, when their father comes home on leave with his footsteps heavy even there, and his back still slightly stooped. They will welcome him with joy, and, Brother Ernst, you must not avoid their eyes. Whosoever walks this earth carries his guilt with him, and that is the unfathomable law of our nature. It is a ring of iron: that you must understand.

Now the illusion ceases to be that of a band of children, for the cloud has become longer and lower, and it is a human body, the body of a sleeping man. Also it is no longer silver, but a brownish yellow, growing darker. Perhaps it is Baranowski, the body in the coffin? Or is it the future that is meant, the future that today is hidden but that is to be revealed? Has Melanie conceived a child in this past night? And will the old prophecy here apply: that before this child has learned to tell good from bad, these present powers of evil will have been destroyed?

But there, too, is Kartuschke. And I know that it must be a long, long road before the hate-ridden shall be redeemed. Life shall not cease to urge us on in the building of that road. And no man will be at peace until he has played his full part in that great work.

For some time we had been flying at a constant altitude, immediately beneath the blackening cloud. Then the nose of the plane turned upward, and we were through and out into the sphere of perfect brightness. Pushing back the turret roof I leaned out and breathed deeply. It was a sort of exultation, a strange, fierce joy. And when, a little later, the pilot took us down again, diving through the cloud bank, and raindrops stung my face like little whiplashes or needle pricks, I did not think to close the roof. I was in harmony with everything, even the wild tumult of the winds.

Albrecht Goes ❦ THE BURNT OFFERING

[1]

THESE PAGES EVOKE THINGS PAST. BUT TO WHAT END? NOT TO perpetuate hatred. Only to raise up a sign in obedience to the eternal sign which commands: "Thus far and no further." A commemorative sign inscribed—on what and for whom? Oh, he writes on air who remembers them, them whose earthly part has passed away, dust and ashes in the earth and wind. Men have forgotten. And indeed one must forget, for how could one go on living if one could not forget? Yet at times there is need of one who remembers. For this is more than ashes in the wind. This is a flame. The world would freeze to death if it were not for this flame.

If it hadn't been for that business with the baby carriage, coming on top of everything, I don't think I should have done it. Human beings are so unfeeling, sir, more unfeeling than cattle. Take any beast—I know how a beast takes notice when one of its mates is getting the knife—I had to go out to the slaughterhouse often enough when my husband was away with the army. Yes, dumb creatures take notice all right. But as for us,

103

we say, things like that oughtn't to be allowed to happen; or we say, but this is terrible, and then we get used to it. And in the business they also say, clients are clients and good money is good money. And besides, I never really knew anything about the Jews; in these parts there were only two families, Dr. Rosenbaum's at No. 12, just on the other side of the road, but they went off to Holland as soon as Hitler came to power; his profession was something like yours, sir, he was a head librarian, I think—those Rosenbaums and that little Miss Wolf, but she'd started keeping her own company by then, and that's why it took them so long to find out she'd turned on the gas . . . it was getting on toward 1938. No, I can't say I knew anything about them; I don't say that to excuse myself, it wouldn't excuse very much in any case, we should have taken more trouble to find out, I know, at least I know it now. As for the new lords and masters, I didn't have much respect for them. They came rattling in to buy a quarter of liver sausage or cold cuts, I wrapped it up for them and said: "Good day." And my husband said, "Heil Hitler!" So we sometimes had words over this. "Now you've done it again," my husband said, "not using the proper form of greeting. And that was the Kreisleiter's lady in person." So I said, "And who might that be, the Kreisleiter's lady in person?" "Don't get too big for your boots," my husband said then, "Dachau is not as far away as you think." So I asked, "Dachau—what's that?" Yes, sir, that's what I asked him, for I really didn't know, and that was as late as '35 or '36. Then my husband said, "Dachau—that's something you won't find in your prayer book." So I kept quiet and asked no more questions.

That's how it was in the first few years. Till the day—it was in December '38, I remember the day quite well, it was a very cold day—when the very first woman came in wearing the yellow star on her coat. She came in just when the lunch hour was over, and I was alone in the shop. "Half a pound of beef, please," she said, keeping an eye on the door all the time, as if someone were after her. "Do you want it on the bone?" I asked her, as I always do, and then I saw the star on her coat, very neatly sewn on with yellow thread it was, strong enough to last her a lifetime. "Yes, please, on the bone," she said. And I get it ready for her, she pays for it, says "Good afternoon" and leaves the shop. But in the evening—I remember this too as if it had happened yesterday—my husband had put away the paper and was fiddling about with the radio, I asked him, "What really went on the other day at the synagogue, and why couldn't you put out the fire?" At that time he was serving in the auxiliary fire service, and they'd got the alarm that night in November. "That's simple," my husband said, "when we'd never fixed the hose to the hydrant." "And why not?" I asked. "Why not," my husband said, and his face turned as white as a sheet, "you shouldn't ask too many questions. Don't worry your head, Greta," he went on, "all that's over and done with."

But by that time I'd already got up and gone out the door, and—without troubling to put on a coat—I went out and walked all around our part of the town, for an hour or more. I could see lights in St. Peter's Church—it was still standing then—so I stood on the steps for a moment and listened to the singing, and then I knew how things would turn out, just as they did turn out six years later, almost to the very day. "Is that how you went out?" my husband asked when I got back, "without so much as a scarf round your neck? You can catch your death that way!" And I said, "That's right, my death."

The war started and my husband had to leave at once, on the second day. It had done him no good to join the Party just before, and when he told them at the recruiting center that being a butcher was a vital occupation, they said to him, "Yes, but you've got a wife to look after the business, and she knows her job." All the same he was discharged again, just after the Polish campaign, only they got him back in February, 1940, and from then on I was all alone here till fall 1947—he was a prisoner of war till then. The first months of the war—everyone was very busy then, there were so many regulations, and you had to keep them all in your head; I must have spent two evenings every week just sticking on the ration-card coupons. There wasn't any time to sit back and think about things, and I was almost glad there wasn't. There were customers who said things like this: "Just you wait, they'll soon give you a fine butcher's shop in Paris or London. Believe me, by the tenth of October we'll be in London, my brother got it straight from headquarters." I never said a word in answer to such foolish talk, only looked up at St. Peter's sometimes, you could just see the tip of the spire through the big shop window, and then I thought to myself: how long?

And then—the day when two men from the political department came in, two young louts I should say, golden pheasants is what they called their sort; people were always inventing funny nicknames like that, but they shouldn't have done . . . well, those fellows produced a sheet of paper. "Gauleiter's orders," they said. A Gauleiter, you probably still remember, was someone very much like the Lord God Almighty in those days. "What about?" I asked, and had a nasty taste in my mouth. "You have been selected for a very special task, Frau Walker," one of them began, and the other: "And this special task requires a very special kind of political tact, you might say." I hadn't the faintest idea what they wanted me to do. "Well, what is it, then?" I asked. "You're going to be the Jews' butcher," one of them said now—I can still see him standing there, a great fat lout with yellow horn-rimmed glasses, not thirty years old, and the other screamed like an echo, "The Jews' butcher," and then they burst out laughing as if they'd told me a particularly good joke: "The Jews' butcher, the Jews' butcher," and just couldn't stop themselves. At last they told me the rest: from now on all the Jews in the town would only be allowed to buy their meat in my shop, and on Fridays, every Friday afternoon between five and seven, my shop would be kept open for the "non-Aryan population," as they called it. "You will prove yourself worthy of this trust." That sounded like a threat and was probably meant that way. The two louts brought out their cigarette cases, sniffed about a bit, threw a few more silly remarks at me ("Don't think you're going to feed Abraham and Sarah veal cutlets and steaks") and took off.

The next day this sinister bit of news appeared in a list of local instructions, and the day after it was the topic of all my customers' conversation. Here I must say there were quite a few of them who didn't like this order and who just looked embarrassed when others talked about it. Some even made no bones about saying what they thought of it. "I only wonder what all this will lead to," one woman might say; and another: "Something pretty bad, you can be sure." "As sure as you're standing here," a third one joined in. But then suddenly somebody called out, I don't remember if it was a man or a woman: "Only be sure you give the place a good airing on Fridays, or no Christian will be able to stand it the next day, Frau Walker." And a young woman—I remember her all right, sir—perked up: "My husband's just home on leave, he'd like to know whether you wouldn't like him to lend you his gas mask for next Friday night." Well, if I wasn't wise till then to what was brewing up, I certainly had a good idea now.

On Friday between one and five my shop was to be closed—this, too, was printed on the instruction sheet, and I still know very well what I felt like that first Friday afternoon. Immediately after closing the shop at one I'd given the stone floor a good washing; I couldn't touch my food that day, but I felt like having a nap. Well, you know that life sometimes does you a good turn, and you doze off in the midst of your terrors. I really did go to sleep, but it was a sleep full of bad dreams. I don't want to talk about it, dreams are only dreams and what came later was worse than any dream. Anyway, that's how I spent the hours before opening time. Shortly before five I'd unlocked the door again, I didn't want to keep them waiting outside; but it was a quarter past five before the first customers turned up. I dare say they'd already had some dealings with my other customers and wanted to make sure of not meeting anyone here. Well, that evening I had my first taste of all the things one could experience in my new work: the timid way in which they handed me their ration cards across the counter, those little colored rags of paper, a different color each month, but every month the same big "J" was printed on them, the same impudent "J" that stood for "Jew," and what they could buy for those cards wasn't enough from the very start to keep body and soul together. Of course they didn't know me, and so they followed every movement of my scissors mistrustfully as I cut out the week's coupons. Later I understood all this. Their fear and their mistrust. And I understood why some of them were so tired that they had to hold on to the counter. For they'd had to walk for an hour or two to get to my shop, they'd been forbidden to use the trams and on the seats in the Schlosspark there were notices saying: "Not for Jews." Some of them were in a great hurry, I was soon struck by that, but the reason for this too didn't become clear to me till much later: on Friday evenings at six o'clock their Sabbath begins, and an orthodox Jew doesn't like to go about his worldly business at that hour or to be out and on the move. They had chosen that day and shopping hour for the Jews so as to spoil the beginning of their Sabbath for them; I understood this in time, they took good care to make me understand.

For already on the third or fourth Friday I had visitors. Supervision? Supervision isn't really the right word, for they paid hardly any attention to me, at least that's how it seemed. They came in twos or threes, in uniform. They carried a Bible about with them, a real showpiece of a Bible it was, large and heavy. Then they struck a great pose, as though they were going to deliver a sermon, opened the Bible and started declaiming. Not a word of what's in the Bible, mind you, but evil rhymes and verses. "Sow's meat . . ." no, I can't repeat what they said—no, sir, I simply can't. But I still know every one of those verses, that I do. You're surprised that I still know them, are you? No, you're not surprised. Can anyone forget such things? How they stood there, "what a fine fellow I am," was their attitude, young, fair-haired lads, quite good-looking, you know the type—and beside them the others, not much to look at they were, the women with their shopping bags made of pressed paper, their clothes all shabby, and the men not much better, and all of them as if they felt a whip on their backs, but faces—real faces. . . . Just a moment, sir, excuse me a moment, please.

It is time for me to inform you who is speaking here and who I am myself, the man who is listening to it. Well, as far as I am concerned, the introduction will not take me very long. I am an assistant in the Museum Library and live out here in the garden city, in a corner house. I occupy a room on the third floor of that house, a house, by the way, which has only recently been put up again, and the room is a very pleasant one. The woman who faces me, my informant—she herself has mentioned her name already—is Frau Walker, the wife of the butcher and landlord, Karl Walker. As to how it came about that I am listening to her account—and this part of an account can hardly be left unfinished at the point she had reached— this will take a little longer to explain. How does one get to know a story? By being inquisitive. All right, but I don't happen to be inquisitive. Or one gets to know a story if one is concerned with the human lot—anyone's lot, or a certain person's. But is the human lot the concern of an assistant in a museum library? Manuscripts, *incunabula*, facsimiles, first editions—these, it goes without saying, interest him. But no; I say that the human lot is our concern. One isn't a sub-tenant in the house of Frau Walker, the woman with the burn on her face, without asking oneself what sort of a person she is, and what sort of lot was cast for her. One doesn't only walk through her shop on coming home, stopping to buy some tongue or ham for one's supper. If Karl Walker is there, well, in that case it might be enough to exchange those words which are always ready on everyone's lips, which no one need trouble

to search for: "Good evening . . . pretty hot today . . . getting cooler, don't you think. . . . Had a hard day, sir? . . .
What would you like tonight?"

Strange: how does this man come to have this particular
wife? Or, still more strange: how does this woman come to have
this particular husband? A butcher—but does a butcher look
like him? There's something depleted, flattened out, about the
man, rather as if history had run over him like a tractor, leaving nothing but a pair of watery blue eyes and a heavy, weary
mouth. ("Good day. What can I do for you, miss? Pork sausages—yes, they're quite fresh, in today. Very best quality,
none better anywhere.") But who is that woman who helps in
the shop at the busiest times, between nine and half past ten in
the mornings, and after five in the evenings? At those times the
sale of meat and the sale of sausages are separate and the
woman stands on the sausage side, if one may put it like that,
also acting as cashier. Anyone can see that her hands were not
made for the butcher's knife; as for her great dark eyes, what
they were intended for is a different question. Her mouth, a
severe, a—I know no better word—a tell-no-secrets mouth, will
give nothing away. Yet there can be no doubt: it is she who is
in charge, responsible here. I remember it well: when I in-
quired about the room in reply to an advertisement and asked
Herr Walker about it—it was some time in the early afternoon
and I found no one there but the man, a short, rather stocky
man in a striped butcher's jacket, black and white—I was told,
"You'd better talk to the lady," and I remember how this
"with the lady" struck me: this was just how an elderly shop
assistant speaks about his female employer, and later events
confirmed my first impression. So I went to see the lady, a little
apprehensive from the first (why, I wonder?), opened the door
which Herr Walker had indicated and came to a room—it ad-
joined the shop—half office, half living room: there I found
Frau Walker, busy with her typewriter. She listened to my request, gave my face a searching, unsmiling look—it was like a
test—and led me to the room. It was a room on the third floor,

bright and with a pleasant view. The furniture—a couch, a wardrobe, a table, a washstand and chairs—was of light natural wood and obviously quite new. What struck me was the absence of little embroidered or crochet-work mats, of family portraits on the walls and other suburban horrors of that kind; instead, there was a reading lamp of the latest design and, as the sole ornament on the wall, an excellent reproduction of Rembrandt's *Tobias*. "I should think you'll prefer to put in other things to suit your own taste," Frau Walker said, and as she said it I decided then and there to take the room.

Once again: who is this woman? If it was my task to find an answer to this question—as, indeed, it is for question and answer that we come up against one another on our way—she did nothing to facilitate this task, nothing, or next to nothing. We rarely had occasion to exchange more than a word of greeting; I did not come face to face with her every day—far from it, as I did not particularly like coming in through the shop. Rather, it had happened once or twice that neighbors tried to draw me into conversation and showed an unmistakable desire to find out something about my landlady. In fact—as I now recall—it was not in Frau Walker's account that I first heard the words "Jews' butcher." "*Where* did you say you live?" somebody asked me the other day, half incredulously, half inquisitorially, and, when I told him, retorted, "Oh, I see, in the Jews' butcher's house"; but then, without giving me time to question him in my turn, he asked again, "And Frau Walker—how is she doing these days?" Whereupon—what else could I do—I put an end to the conversation with some noncommittal remark and took my leave. This woman and her past—what was her past?—this is not a topic to be discussed over the garden wall, as one knows well enough without knowing how one came to know it.

The next thing—I am trying to remember the sequence of events—was our meeting one evening at the "Pro Israel" Society, an association that has made it its business to prepare the ground for the renewal of genuine relations with Israel.

A colleague at the library had introduced me to it, and I was not a little astonished when I discovered my landlady among those taking part in the small gathering, not, indeed, as an occasional guest, as I could see at once, but as a well-informed member. In the room itself we could only exchange a silent greeting, but it so happened that we walked home together and that our conversation returned to the evening's discussions. "Speak ye comfortably to Jerusalem!" I took up the speaker's motto again and said, "But that, of course, is not so easy . . . I am thinking of the young generation in our country, to whom one would like to be of some use. They hardly have such a thing as convictions or a point of view any more, and to love ideas for their own sake is very hard indeed." Frau Walker replied, "Even so, a few of the exiles have returned, so we should make those few aware of how we feel about them. And anyway, if only one or two of us remain alive to the meaning of the terror, this too will not be in vain." As she said this, I looked at her sideways and could clearly see that she was talking about a terror that was wholly alive in *her:* the terror, the state of being terrified by everything of which human beings are capable. I was on the point of asking her how she had come to join this "Pro Israel" Society, but it isn't so easy to ask Frau Walker anything. Besides, we were almost back at the house. My landlady unlatched the door, we said good night in the hallway. Since then a fortnight has passed, and no other encounter offered itself.

But today . . . I walk into the sitting room, my glance, like the glance of every man in my profession, runs along the bookcase and is caught by a Hebrew title on the spine of one book. A book in Hebrew? Well, there I'm on my own ground, so I can touch the book without being thought impertinent and ask her: "How did that book come your way?" "That's a long story," she said, but there must have been something in my glance, something quite different from mere curiosity, that made her add: "I'll tell it to you one day." Then I said—it was in the evening, we were standing beside her chest of drawers, one could hear the silence of the house like a voice beyond time—and I said, "Now."

And so she began to tell her story, or rather to evoke it from the depths. That is not to say that what followed now ("If it hadn't been for that business with the baby carriage . . .") poured out of her like a waterfall. No, it would be truer to say that she hauled it up out of a deep shaft. She told her story slowly and with long pauses. Waterfall or shaft—no matter; she was speaking, and it was not fitting to interrupt her while she spoke. As long as she was silent, I heard the clock ticking, time steadily passing. Time that is grace and judgment. Already judgment. Still grace.

"Just a moment, sir, excuse me a moment, please," she had said then and left the room. Not a sound had reached me from the world outside, as no sound would reach one down in a mine. Somebody must have come in, Herr Walker or a visitor. Now she returned, dressed to go out, a Red Cross bag in her hand. "I have to leave quickly for a neighbor's house," she said, "they've had an accident, a child scalded its arm. That's a kind of relic of the war years, I mean being called in for cases of that sort," she added with a faint smile.

She was right back in the present and her thoughts, most probably, were already occupied with the child. Our conversation had been broken off. Conversation, I suppose, is the wrong word; she had done the talking, but if listening is a different form of speaking, it was a conversation indeed. She hadn't said: "I'll be back in no time, please wait here." Nor had she said, what she could easily have said: "That will have to be all for now; more another day." But the opening sentence of her account was something to which I could go back myself, something like a promise of a sequel to her story. Not a pleasant story—that much is certain even now. But, then, who says that one cannot draw some light from a gloomy story, as one strikes bright fire from dark stone?

[2]

AT ONCE, I SAID TO MYSELF, I MUST HEAR THE END OF THE STORY at once. Even for Frau Walker's sake I mustn't delay it too long. A person who has the courage to expose such experiences to the light of day, once they are safely buried, opens up, like the body of a woman in childbirth. Soon the trap door must close again. But not until someone has been let into the secret. I was that person.

Our conversation had taken place on a Tuesday; on Wednesday and Thursday nights I had professional engagements and I could no longer cancel my acceptance of an invitation for Friday night. There were eleven of us in the house of a County Court judge, the buffet supper was excellent and so was the dry Moselle wine, we had chamber music, a sprightly trio by a French composer of the seventeenth century, a flute sonata by Couperin and something by Mozart at the end; there was the good conversation of open-minded persons in which I should have taken part with pleasure at any other time—but how could I enjoy a ham sandwich when my ears buzzed with "Half a pound of beef, please!" and what does Mozart sound like on this devastated earth ("You are going to be the Jews' butcher!")? Also I wasn't interested in hearing the County Court judge's opinions on Byzantine mosaics—I wanted to know whether he had punished one of those who set fire to the synagogue, or would have punished him, I should probably say.

A fever was creeping over me, I could feel it now in my spine, now on my temples; I took my leave early, went home and endured the long night as best I could. At last it was day and I knew at once that it would turn into one of those days on which one's life and destiny get more deeply under one's skin than on other days. A fever has eaten away some of our power of resistance, we cannot choose among the things that happen to us, but just for that reason such days are rarely insignificant or a mere waste of time. The house in which we live and which often enough is nothing more to us than so many floors piled one above the other, so many instructions and prohibitions ("Don't leave the light on all night," "Kindly wipe your shoes," "Shut the door after you, please"), nothing more than a conglomeration of letter boxes and milk bottles—suddenly it is the house of destiny, life leaps at me from every door, a panther, an enemy, an ally, a life that I love—as ever. Everyone who lives there concerns me, I share life with them all, I am their companion, their friend; the breath they draw affects me, my heartbeat responds to theirs. We are no longer divided by that wall, and what at other times is simply a source of irritation or worse—the sound of electric switches next door, the sighs, the thumps and shouts, the conflict of words, the message of their love-hate—all expressions of the life of the young couple, musicians both of them, who share the third floor with me—suddenly all this affects me differently: the inexpressible gravity with which the life of strangers touches upon one's own pervades everything. Suddenly the girl accountant on the first floor is no longer the rather pert occupant of number 5, but that which in truth she is at every hour, whether she knows it or not: a life that seeks fulfillment. Suddenly Karl Walker too is a real person, without the mask of security, a troubled man.

Today, then, in the evening I shall go down to Frau Walker's room and ask her to tell me the end of her story, if one calls it the end ("If it hadn't been for that business with the baby carriage"). Today, as my own defenseless frame of mind, this unusual susceptibility to the lives of others, will assure, I shall understand that this story, whatever horrors it may contain, signifies love in its innermost recesses, that love which maintains the world.

But that evening Sabine arrived. Which Sabine? There are seven Sabines inside that one Sabine. No, probably more than seven, one can't claim to know the whole of her just because one has been working with her for a year and spent an occasional evening with her outside working hours. "The room brightens up when Fräulein Sabine comes in," that's the formula for one of the Sabines, I have heard it more than once, out of the head librarian's mouth, for instance. "But really, she's the most mysterious creature on God's earth"; that refers to another of the Sabines. Sabine the practical, Sabine the ruler—yes, she can rule all right, at her desk at the library above all; Sabine the high-spirited—but very few know of *her*. Still more rarely does one meet Sabine the timid, the fugitive. If one could see the whole of her one might call her Sabine the guest.

As for her past, here are a few outlines, all that I know of it; only as much as one learns from a friend, flashes of lightning that give you a glimpse of the landscape, a breath or two of changeless air. (So-called "complete records" are a matter for the police or, as one would once have said, for the family album.) Well, then: Sabine Berendson, daughter of a Jewish publisher and his non-Jewish wife, born in 1928, in outward appearance takes after her mother: tall, ash-blond hair, blue eyes; in her character—but how can I say, in her character she takes after her father, when I have no other knowledge of that father than what I gathered from Sabine's scanty account? She spoke of this father, who lives at Cambridge, as one speaks of the heroes of legends, to be more precise, of legends about the saints. By perilous ways, disguised as an Aryan, Sabine had survived the Hitler regime; when no other resort was left to them, her parents had agreed on a merely formal separation, for the sake of their daughter's future. "Till the evil spell is broken," they had said, but then the mother had died on an April day in 1945, died at a moment when dying had ceased to be a personal matter (engulfed with the rest, dug in with the rest), while Sabine was away on "compulsory foreign service"— that's what they called it then—leaving no news, no death certificate, no description of the grave and, strangely enough, no very deep impression on her daughter's memory. Her father had been able to flee the country at a moment when no other means of survival seemed possible for persons of his kind. One autumn evening in the year 1945—all unforgettable, day and hour, weather and color of the sky—she received news that he was alive; the British Commandant of the town had passed it on to her; it was like a second birth, *incipit vita nova*. But here and now Sabine was alone, very much alone, Sabine the guest.

The guest: a person who feels a deep kinship with the ephemeral things of this life and will never understand the meaning of goods and chattels, safety of bolt and lock. There's the special way in which she hangs up her duffel coat on entering the room, as if making sure that she can take it down again without loss of time; there's the special way in which she follows the smoke of her cigarette with her eyes, blue cloud, adieu . . . . To bring you a bunch of flowers is something that would occur to her easily, to bring you something more lasting, a cactus plant, say, never. And so in all things. She'll never take to the idea of a fine collection of phonograph records ("Oh, my dear fellow, there's your stock of canned goods again"), but she's always chasing the radio waves at night. ("Do you remember: tocktocktocktock; *hier ist London, hier ist London, hier ist London?*") Photographic feats she despises utterly: "Not for me," she says. "That is for people who have to hang on to time, who're afraid of losing their faces." Telephone calls, on the other hand, long conversations with long pauses, are something after her own heart. "Wonderful, how it makes words reach their right place, the only place worthy of them, the wholly imaginary." Which of these Sabines might be coming today?

She came with her head in a cloud—never disturb the other when his head is in a cloud, that's an unwritten law of friendship—took off her coat, asked for a cigarette, and filled the kettle. Then she took the tea from the shelf and set the table for us both; it was like a silent ritual. For a moment, three moments in all, just till the water boiled, she made herself comfortable on the couch. To be here, to be accepted and borne up, three floors up, thirty floors up, as high as love can—but without forgetting that we're on our way, that this is only a way station. A station lasting as long as a heartbeat, perhaps as long as a kiss. She looked at me; Sabine the guest. And suddenly I knew what it meant, and understood all at once where Sabine belongs. She is part of Frau Walker's story. I don't yet know the place. (Really I must hear the end of that story. Tonight, perhaps? No, not tonight. This is Sabine's hour.) But what is her place in the story?

"Tell me, Sabine, where did you spend the summer of '42?"

"The summer of '42? I was at Offenbach, still at school. Fourth form, no, already the fifth. And then, the beginning of September, I came here."

"You came here?"

"Yes. My father urgently wanted us to get swallowed up in a large city, my mother and myself. He thought there'd be a better chance here, a better chance of getting me through it all unmolested, as he hoped. 'I tell you, we'll manage it after all,' he said a few times before the separation, looking at me in a way I can't describe. 'The very image of Germania,' he said. 'And once you've dropped the Berendson, I tell you, we'll manage it after all, you'll come through.' They had decided that we should be known by my mother's surname. Uncanny that: to give up one's name. One never knows what else one's giving up with it."

"But you must have known even then what the game was, and that it wasn't a 'game'?"

"Yes . . . and no. Yes, I suppose I understood. At first I wanted to say that everything was quite different at the time from what it seems like in retrospect. My father, you see, my father loved Germany. He'd fought in the First World War. My father . . . yes, that's what he's like: he simply doesn't know how to hate. In our house we lived as if we were on an island. My father wore the yellow star, but he wore it like a decoration. I've never seen Father angry, only silent. I'll tell you the story about Rebecca, then you'll understand what things were like at that time. And what Father was like. Rebecca—but I can't tell you the story in such a loud voice. Come a bit nearer—"

I sat down on the couch, Sabine put her arms around my neck and continued her story in a whisper, as if there were a stranger in the room who must not be allowed to overhear what she said. Perhaps that stranger was Death, or the enemy, or the specter of fear.

"Rebecca, then. At that time, at Offenbach, Rebecca was my friend, it was the only time I really had a friend; on the whole I'm not very good at keeping up friendships, people always demand too much. Rebecca was the daughter of the cantor in the synagogue, and she looked just like Rebecca at the well, you can probably imagine what that was like—you know: 'Both drink thou, and I will also draw for thy camels.' She was only a year older than I was, but really she was years older, for she already had a genuine life of her own. When the arrests began, the cantor and his wife hid their daughter, always sending her to a different family; people could be trusted to keep a secret, it worked pretty well. A few times she stayed with us too, we had long conversations before going to sleep, they were the kind one doesn't easily forget. But then suddenly Rebecca had vanished. 'Where's Rebecca?' I asked them every day, morning, noon and night; I knew: without Rebecca the world was not the same. She's gone away, my mother said, and it wasn't even untrue. She *had* gone away, to Auschwitz, I think, to the gas chamber—but my mother said nothing about that. People should tell the truth, but I don't blame them for not telling me the whole truth then. 'Where's Rebecca?' I remember asking. I was alone in the room with my father and asked the question for the twentieth, for the thirtieth time: 'Where's Rebecca?' And my father replied, 'In you.' And that's all he said. It was as if he wanted to give me time to—how shall I put it—to spell it out; 'In you.' And only after a little pause he added, 'One doesn't lose people whom one loves so much.' Then I understood, as far as one would at thirteen or fourteen, and I remember that I kissed his hand. He took me in his arms. By that time he'd already made up his mind about the separation, and when I think of that moment now, I know

that all this was already contained in the way he looked at me
and consoled me, and in his words. He was already living like
a fugitive; he worked in a small back room now, the main office
was occupied by his successors. Even at home we saw next to
nothing of him, he crept into his own house late at night. But
what his look meant to tell me that day was: 'I shan't lose you
either.' "

"I shan't lose you either." Sabine was silent. There was
nothing more to be said about Offenbach and nothing more
about her father. History was extinguished, as a candle is extinguished; the present revealed its face, a holy and mighty
face. "If only it would stay like that"; these are simple words,
the simplest of all. We both thought them, and each of us
knew that the other was thinking them. But we did not say
them.

"Another cigarette, if you don't mind. And let's have some
music; couldn't you look for something good?" I switched on
the radio and let the dial travel from name to name; Europe's
transmitters released their flow of gurgling soapsuds, indigest-
ible all of it; but here—stop—and Sabine too cried "Stop!"—
this was music, truly perfect nocturnal music, Locatelli or
Cimarosa. "What is it, Sabine? It isn't Mozart, it must be earlier, less encumbered."

"Oh, don't worry about it, my dear. No need to stick labels
on it. Let's just be glad it's there at all, that it is as it is and
that there's a place for it in the world, a healthy place among
all the scabs and pus. It won't last us very long, but at least it
exists."

Who knows Sabine? She had turned toward the window and
only glanced at me for a moment between two gulps of air that
were almost sighs. Then she came up to me, kissed me once
more, but only as in parting, and said, "Did you know you've
got my father's eyes? Another reason for coming to see you
from time to time." And then, in a different tone of voice:
"Excuse this nonsense, just one feminine tear and a half. Too
silly of me. What do you say to a short walk?"

"A good idea, Sabine. Let's go."

We were standing in the hallway, I was looking for my key, when the door was opened from the outside; Frau Walker had come home. We said good evening; I wondered whether I ought to introduce Sabine, it was the first opportunity and it seemed suitable enough. Frau Walker looked up at Sabine, something seemed to be going on in her face, and she said, "Excuse me, miss, and you too, sir, must excuse me, but— you're Sabine Berendson, aren't you?"

"Yes." The "yes" was almost a gasp.

"And your father?"

"My father?" (This is even weirder than I thought.) "My father lives in England—at Cambridge . . ."

"Then your father's alive. I'm so happy to hear it."

"But—"

We had no chance to ask further questions. What we saw now was that face with curtains drawn which I knew from Tuesday last, and really I had known it long before that Tuesday evening. At a face like that one doesn't fire questions. "How do you come to know me? I don't think we've ever met. And how do you come to know my father?" Such questions may present themselves. But no question is permitted.

Meanwhile Frau Walker had unlocked her glass door. "Good night," she said, nodding at us, and added, "Have a good time together." We liked the sound of this "together." The special sound it has for two people who are seeking their way. We walked out into a fine evening rain and felt as if Frau Walker's "together" were keeping watch over us.

"How extraordinary!" It was I who broke the silence. "I really don't know what to say. That it makes me believe in clairvoyance is the least of it. There you stand for a moment on the threshold, in the dimness of the hallway light, and a strange woman tells you you're Sabine Berendson. And how did she find out anything about your father?"

"That's the most incomprehensible thing of all. True, my father's been here once or twice, years ago, for interviews with publishers, I think, for a day or two at a time. He liked the

town, that I know, and the countryside too, and that may be
why he chose to send us here of all places, but how on earth
could he have run into Frau Walker?"

"And then she said: 'You're Sabine Berendson, aren't
you?' "

"Of course my face may not be altogether unknown to her.
If someone so openly displays one's photograph on his chest of
drawers, as you do, then the landlady, who most probably
tidies up your room from time to time, may recognize that face,
possibly even in the hallway at night. But my father's name—
how does she come to know his name? You must find out. No, *I*
must find it out. I shall write to my father."

[3]

WHY DID IT OCCUR TO ME THAT THERE WAS A LETTER FOR ME IN
the box by the staircase, now, at this late hour? The light in
the hallway had gone out at the moment I withdrew my key
from the front-door latch, after returning from my walk with
Sabine. I had climbed my three flights of stairs in the dark, put
everything back in its place—not without great sadness, as
usual—made up my couch for the night. Could it be that there
was a letter for me in the box downstairs?

For a time one struggles against inertia, one's reluctance to
climb the stairs again, and calls on reason to support it by
arguing that no one delivers letters at such a late hour, but
suddenly one does find oneself on the stairs, ready to pursue
the mirage.

It is not a mirage. There *is* a letter. A letter with no stamps
and no sender's address. I did not know the hand that had
written my two names on the envelope, but before I had
opened it, I knew: this is a letter from Frau Walker.

Was I surprised? By the fact that she had written to me? By

the handwriting itself, the freedom and assurance of its sweep? No, I was not surprised. I had been surprised when I heard myself saying "now," that somehow challenging "now" of the other night; for willingly and consciously I had entered the shaft whose name is: the Unheard-of, the Unpredictable. Now it was not for me to wonder at anything that might happen.

This is her letter:

Dear Sir: Since you came to see me everything that had been left in the dark for years has been stirred up again. There was a time when I could not face these things, even in thought. But now it seems almost a good thing that I've been forced to face them again, and I want to tell you more about them; in writing this is a little easier than by word of mouth. For when I sit facing the sheet of paper, I have time to wait for them to come again, stay for a while and move on—I mean the people of those years—and I think to myself: as long as I write about them and as long as you read about them, tomorrow or the day after, these people are really with us again. Of course I know that it won't be much of a letter.

I've already told you that I knew next to nothing about the Jews. It was only by having all this wretched business thrown at me every Friday evening that I found out about them. And I understood where a decent person belongs, and discovered what a decent person must do. Or rather I soon knew what one ought to have done, what was the proper thing to have done. But, then, we all failed to do this proper thing. At the very most, if all went well, we threw a little drop of water into a roaring fire. Sometimes a soldier on leave gave you a meat coupon or two, and those you then shared out on a Friday evening, so that one or another of them got a little snippet more than the tiny amount to which he was entitled by the card. Those ration cards: if you had to handle them week after week, you learned to read them like a book. For instance, there might be a card that differed from the others in giving the owner a little supplement, a handful of barley, it might be, or a quarter pound of bread—but how dearly they had to pay for such beggar's fare. The man entitled to it was forced to work in an arms factory, happily employed in producing munitions. And what were those used for? For the "fateful combat," as they called it; but also for the mass executions over there in the East. And the man who produced cartridges here knew it well enough. Or else I was handed two children's ration cards across the counter. But I didn't see the cards with all their blank spaces, what I saw was the children themselves and their out-lawed lives: each of them standing alone in his back yard, not understanding why his playmates act like a lot of strangers. "Come over and play with me!" And the other voice replies, "My mother said I mustn't play with you any more. German boys don't play with a Jew-boy, she said." One day someone's left a foul drawing on a school desk and a word goes round the class, an insulting word; "shickse," they say, children are cruel, and the *Stürmer* on the notice board has long ago made sure that even the youngest are well-informed.

And then there's the old man who doesn't understand at all. It takes him a long time to find his ration card in his pocket, and longer to spread it out on the counter. He seems aston-ished all the time, as he looks round with a half-smile, but this half-smile cuts into your soul. "Germans—goot people, Ger-mans—not bat," he says to me, in the accent and intonation of Czenstochau in Poland; I feel a lump in my throat, and I don't say what I'm thinking: Germans bad.

Now, sir, don't say: that Frau Walker is delirious. I'm not delirious, though I am seeing things. I can see them standing in front of my counter, eight or ten or twelve of them at a time. Women, children, and old men—the younger men have be-come very rare; I get to know their names and read their faces; whether I read them aright, I can't say, but I suppose you can learn anything if you practice long enough. "Well, what are they like, then, your Friday night Jews?" someone would ask from time to time. "Just an alien mob, aren't they? And sinis-ter? And unkempt?"

Alien? Yes, they feel alien enough. And unkempt. But let anyone try to keep clean without enough soap, without washing facilities, without textiles, without new leather. And sinister? No, not sinister, only sad, very sad. I'm reminded of the children, the first two, who spent half an hour in my sitting room, the selfsame room in which we talked the other night. I'd noticed that two mothers had other shopping to do elsewhere and that their children were almost too tired to go with them. "The children can wait here till you come back," I'd said to the two women, opening the door to this small room. "You sit down here like good girls," I said to them, and it was quite a while before I could see to them again, for I was kept pretty busy trying to serve everyone, at least for the first few months. After that—but I'll come to that later. At last I had a free moment and went in to see what the children were doing. There they were, still sitting together on a single chair, and it was obvious that they hadn't stirred from their places. I cut up part of a wartime cake, we ran to cake of a sort from time to time; they looked at me incredulously when I offered them the plate: "Share it between you!" Their mothers came back and called the children; they wouldn't shake hands with me, but the two mothers gave me a long look; almost hostile, I thought, this look was—but what do we know about such things? Whether they were alien to me, people had asked me, those Friday evening Jews. (But excuse me, sir, I've already written about that; you must understand that it isn't easy for me to keep to one thread.) Well, they were alien to me; but when people spoke with so much commiseration and mistrust about "my Jews," I should have liked to answer back, "That's right, they're my Jews."

I've already told you about those other visitors who would arrive so suddenly from time to time. As long as they were there, none of my customers would say anything that wasn't absolutely necessary, but there were Fridays when no patrol came our way, and then they'd talk to me. I never asked them to talk, but neither did I turn a deaf ear when they did talk.

All I knew was that they needed someone who'd listen to them. Even if he couldn't do anything to help them.

That's how it was at the start. But then came that business with the wrapping paper. Frau M.—I still know her name, but I got so used to abbreviations, I'll put one here if you don't mind—Frau M. was one of the most refined of my Friday evening customers, and at the same time she was one of the bluntest, if you can say any of them was blunt. When most of these customers were already talking to me quite openly, she never said a word that could be left unsaid. In fact I hardly knew the sound of her voice—till the day when she quite unexpectedly addressed me, and came out with a whole sentence. "My sister-in-law is coming later," she said. "She'll collect my ration. Keep it for her, please, and"—she hesitated—"and wrap up the meat in this," pulling a piece of gray wrapping paper out of her handbag. I wanted to reply, "Don't trouble yourself, there's no need—there's no shortage of wrapping paper yet," but she said, "Please!" And this "Please!" was so severe that I could only nod my head and do what she asked. Her sister-in-law never came that day, and the gray paper was still on the counter when I closed the shop. I picked it up and was just about to wrap up the meat in it, as Frau M. had asked me to do, when I discovered a pencilled note on the gray paper. It read: "Sigi is gone, Theresienstadt, Block XVII, will you write to him—Love M."

Did I mention that on her way out Frau M. had turned her head and said "Many thanks," just those two words, loud and distinct?

On the following Friday—I was worried about this business —the sister-in-law appeared. I had to be very careful that day, as the visitors had come, and somehow I was more conscious than usual of being under observation; I dare say it was a kind of premonition. I took advantage of a moment when the SS Men were talking to each other to say: "Your sister-in-law left her ration behind last time she was here. She asked me to keep it for you. Do you think Frau M. herself will be coming today?

If not, I could let you have something else as well. I've made a note of the amount." If only those young fellows don't get interested in us, I thought, and I felt my heart throb in my throat. "Frau M. doesn't need her ration any more," her sister-in-law said very quickly; a slight motion of her hand toward her throat told me everything. That was the kind of language we used in those days. I knew at once: they've taken the husband away, the wife scribbles a brief note to inform her sister that the man has been "transported," and then she goes off and does away with herself. Can I be sure the overseers haven't noticed this motion of the woman's hand? They have not, thank God! They go to the door and take their leave in the terms they think fitting. "Perish Judea!" they bawl out, and then, "Heil Hitler!"

Now it strikes me how curious it was that the others hardly talked among themselves, as if the general terror had taken hold of them too and estranged one from another. And at times it really looked like that, as if they distrusted one another. For a time I even suspected that it was one of themselves who had been partly responsible for having the rabbi "transported." You see, sir, from that place behind the counter one really had a good view of the world in those days, I mean the real world outside in which all things can happen, the best and the worst. That Dr. Ehrenreich must have known too that all things are possible, that you can't even rely on being safe with your own people, but of course he couldn't have acted otherwise than he did.

I stopped here for a while, to rest my hand. I looked out of the window, and that recalled the war nights. That's how one used to stand in the dark, listening up into the sky, listening for the planes at night. Then I started rereading these last pages myself, and I notice that I haven't told you anything about that rabbi yet; as I said, you must excuse me if this story reads like a crazy jumble of events—as far as I'm concerned, Rabbi Ehrenreich was present again all the time I was writing.

I've already told you how I wondered why they hardly spoke

to one another; and the first reason why I took notice of the rabbi was just that they always hailed him when he came in and spoke to him, even if they spoke to no one else. I should never have known he was a rabbi, for in appearance—at least in dress— he didn't differ from other old men. The shopping net he carried was usually heavy by the time he came to the shop. He had to buy all the rations for seven or eight people, every time. What did he look like? He looked like—well, at the time I didn't know, as I hadn't yet started reading the Bible properly, I only knew it suddenly when I came to read the Book of Jeremiah; that's what he looked like, the prophet Jeremiah himself. Usually he came on the stroke of six. One day, I remember, the bell of St. Peter's—there was only one bell left in the clocktower at that time—had just been rung, and after the ringing there was real silence for a few moments. Then the rabbi spoke one word in a loud voice. I heard the sound clearly, but couldn't understand. Later I learned that word. He had said "Shalom," and when he said it all the people in the shop stood quite motionless. Then he said other words, and I knew it must be a prayer or a text from the Bible, for everyone took part in silence. This had become their synagogue now. I kept very quiet and put the knife away. (My only fear was that the black visitors might come just at that moment; this would mean trouble.) And then suddenly I noticed one customer looking at the rabbi with an evil, a really vicious glance. It was a young fellow who rarely came here, since his mother did most of the shopping. He stepped up to the counter and, in the midst of that silence, said to me in a very loud voice, "How much do I owe you?" I named the sum as quietly as possible but he put the coins on the tray one by one, taking care to produce a loud noise with each, and then said at the top of his voice, "Good evening to you, then," and left the shop. The other customers never turned to look at him, the service went on. But I thought to myself: so that's how it is, with them as well as with us; this is the community, but that young fellow is no longer with it. But what a good thing the black men didn't come today, I thought again.

A week later—everything was the same, only the vicious boy's mother had come in his place and a few of the other customers were different ones—the rabbi spoke the same words, and I myself felt I was taking part in this strange service of which I didn't understand a word; so I forgot my sentry duty—no one had commanded me to be a sentry, but one has to keep some sort of watch over people praying as they flee. The door suddenly opened, at the very moment when the rabbi was extending his arm in blessing; his congregation, still in a sort of trance, couldn't move back quick enough into the everyday world—and the intruders were already in the shop, no less than four of them, too. The leader, a great giant of a man, called out, "Heil Hitler! What's going on in this place? D'you think this is a church or a Jews' brothel or something?" And he went straight up to the rabbi with a threatening gesture.

"Hey, Yid, I'm talking to you!"

And I remember every word of the rest.

"My name is Dr. Ehrenreich," said the rabbi. (That's when it struck me that he looked like a prophet.)

"A Yid is what you are," this giant Goliath shouted, "A filthy bastard of a Jew. What do you think you were doing just now?"

"I was praying."

"That won't get you a sausage to stuff into your belly."

"It isn't for sausages I pray, but for human beings."

"Your lot certainly need to."

"We all need to."

"There's no accounting for tastes. I wouldn't like to be in your dirty mouth, Yid."

"It is not God's will that you should perish."

There was a great silence now, a terrible silence, and all looked on, my customers and the other's companions; it seemed to me that the men in black uniforms were even more startled than those who had been roused from their prayers.

David and Goliath—that's how I thought of them now. And I wondered if the story would really be allowed to end differently in this case. Was it really possible that it should end in this way: that the small and venerable man would be dragged out by his beard and transported, sir, never again to be heard of or seen?

You can imagine the feelings with which I waited for the following Friday night. Some days I considered whether I should report those men, for breaking the peace in a private dwelling, perhaps, but there was not the slightest hope that justice would be done. There was no longer such a thing as justice. Yet at times a delay occurred in the workings of injustice itself; and it is to such delays that many of us owe our lives. The following Friday passed without a visit from the intruders; and quite a number of other Fridays passed quietly enough. Those weeks—I've given a great deal of thought to them since—were no less strange for that. For after this incident my Friday customers began to talk differently among themselves. It was just as if this calamity had loosened all their tongues. And—strange or not strange, I don't know—they began to speak to me too in a different way, different from the first months, I mean. The little living room that had once harbored the two children was never empty now, and it wasn't only on Fridays that we met there. That was about the time, too, when the Hebrew book came my way, the one you found on my bookshelf. A doctor's wife brought it for me, as a parting gift, and you know what sort of a parting that was. It was a pretty risky game I was playing then, there's no doubt about it. And I needn't tell you that it wasn't only a game.

Still another new sheet. I know I'm asking a lot of you, sir, and my handwriting isn't quite what it used to be, as my sight has never quite recovered from the effect of that fire; but, I told you right at the start the other day, it was the business with the baby carriage that brought everything to a head, and that's something I shouldn't be able to talk about if you were sitting just in front of me here.

It was the sixteenth of October; you know the date because it was the day the Museum Library was destroyed, and it was a

Friday. Everything was the same as ever, I stood behind the counter, my customers handed me their ration cards, trustingly now and without fear; they had ceased to pray in the shop since the rabbi's transportation, but sometimes I was the one who said "Shalom" instead of the usual greeting for now I knew well what the word means, and the person addressed would often reply, "Shalom." That was our Sabbath in the butcher's shop. . . . I heard a car draw up; its door was shut with a bang, so that I just had time to call out "Careful!" before Goliath was in the shop. He had been followed by a feeble little fellow stuck into a uniform that didn't seem to belong to him. I went on with my work as if I hadn't noticed them at all, but I saw at once that the giant had been promoted to a higher rank since his last visit; one had learned to pay attention to such things. It was clear that they'd lost no time in rewarding him for his recent feat. By the peculiar fixed gaze he directed at different parts of the shop I could see that he'd been drinking. He lit a cigarette and, after drawing at it, pushed the burning end into an old man's face; the action was so sudden that the first I knew of it was the victim's cry of pain. Now things are going to get bad, I thought, very bad indeed. And I knew at once: I would not be silent in this case. The time for silence was past.

"Smoking is prohibited here by law," I said, stressing the word "law." Our Goliath turned his eyes on me, as if he'd just grown aware of my presence, then he read the printed notice which I'd indicated with a jerk of my head, and to my surprise he trod out the cigarette, though he'd only just begun to smoke it, but with a evil smile on his face. He turned to the customer nearest to him—it was a former judge, long retired. "Are you quite sure you couldn't still get away?" I'd asked him recently, and he'd answered: "No, I can't get away any more, I'm too old; and I don't want to either, my gravestone's waiting for me here." Now I saw the big fellow knock the package of meat out of his hand. "Yid!" he called out, "you'd better not eat too much, or you'll get too heavy for your ascension. You're off on the fifteenth—whiz-bang, you'll fly through the air with the greatest of ease!"

Everyone looked at Goliath. Only two or three customers pretended they hadn't heard, and one of them went up to me to state his order. I couldn't attend to him at once, for I had to see to Frau Zalewsky. She had put her bag on the floor and stood trembling all over. She was a musician's wife and was expecting a baby any day now. I knew quite a bit about her. She'd had the effrontery to apply for the "Supplementary Ration for Expectant Mothers" in the fourth month of her pregnancy, about a half-pint of milk and a few ounces of sugar and flour. Her application had been returned with this statement: "What a Jew's bastard needs is abortion. Apply to the Health Department, Section D." She preserved this document in her handbag and had once shown it to me. I read it, looked carefully at the stamp and signature, even making a mental note of the typist's initials: if one could dictate a sentence like that one to a secretary, there wasn't much one couldn't do. "Frau Zalewsky!" I said now. "Don't worry," she replied, deathly pale, "I'll feel better in a moment." I went back to the customer who—quite unmoved, it seemed—repeated his order. The big fellow started again: "Whiz-bang, whiz-bang, you'll fly through the air with the greatest of ease. . . ." It looked as if he was about to perform some sort of war dance, when his puny, scraggy companion, himself a little David now, took one pace toward the towering great fellow, jumped to attention and said in a very quiet voice, "Untersturmführer, please remember you're on duty."

Goliath opened his eyes wide and shot out one arm. It seemed incredible to him that anyone should dare to put him in his place. And now he erupted: "That's a lot of hogwash! Why, I'm doing them a real favor—don't you start making trouble, Beck, just keep your shirt on, will you—a real favor, I say, breaking it to them gradually—real bedside manner and all—just giving them a delicate hint that they'll soon be going up the chimney. Can't you see, Beck, that Sarah over there with the big belly, she's just beaming with gratitude—aren't you, Sarah?—for telling her she needn't worry any more about the baby's diapers, those dear little shitty diapers—"

"Untersturmführer!" the young man called out again, and it sounded almost as if he was pleading; then he took hold of his superior's arm.

"Hands off, damn you!" he yelled, in a drunken rage, but at the same time made for the door with long unsteady steps. When he'd followed him to the door, the little fellow turned around and called out to me, "You'll keep your mouth shut!" I nodded. Why shouldn't I keep quiet, when the stones themselves would speak?

I continued my work in silence, and no one there said another word that evening. I cut the week's coupons out of the cards and handed the goods across the counter. It came into my head—and even now, after many years, I wonder what made me do it—to give each customer much more than his proper ration. All I remember is that when they'd all gone, and I realized I'd most probably never be able to make up for this loss, I felt relieved and almost cheerful. I could still hear those dreadful words re-echo round the shop, but when I locked the door behind the last customer, I felt as if the whole burden had already been lifted from my shoulders.

An hour had gone by, I was sitting in my room and doing some sewing, when I heard a faint knock at my window. I got up to open the door. I'm not very brave, sir. I was very frightened. It was no longer as I'd thought before, I mean about the burden having been lifted from my shoulders. The burden was still there, as heavy as ever. It was Frau Zalewsky, the musician's wife, who'd come to see me. "Open the door for a moment, please," she said. I unlocked it at once. Frau Zalewsky had stepped back for a moment into the dark side passage and now returned, pushing something toward the door. It was a baby carriage. She pushed it straight through the outer door and into the room, the same room in which I'm writing this down. The baby carriage stood in the very place where you were sitting the other night; and, as far as I'm concerned, it's still standing there. . . .

"Do take a seat, Frau Zalewsky," I said; she sat down, in the awkward way a woman sits down in her last weeks of pregnancy. Then she began: "It's true—it's true what that man said."

"The one who was drunk, you mean?" I wanted it to sound like a doubt, but I'd only to listen to my own voice to know that I'd said it without conviction. The world has become so bad that only the very worst is true.

"Yes, that one," the woman confirmed. "The rabbi once said: 'God created wine to loosen the tongues of fools, that they may speak the truth unto those that seek truth.' "

And then: silence. I kept my eyes lowered. Then the woman's voice again: "I've brought you that baby carriage. You've been good to me all this time. I thought, maybe you'll need it one day, Frau Walker, later, I mean." And again: silence. Then: "I must go now. Thank you again for everything. Where shall we put it?"

"Oh, just leave it where it is, thank you." That's all I could think of saying.

At the front door Frau Zalewsky turned her head once more; it was quite dark now and I could hardly see her, but I heard her voice and thought to myself: a true child of Rabbi Ehrenreich, that's what she's like—no, a true descendant of the ancient prophets. The sky was full of autumn stars that night. The last words I heard her say—and one doesn't forget such words—were so faint, they sounded far away; very softly, she said: "And the word of the Lord came unto Abram, saying: Look now toward heaven, and tell the stars, if thou be able to number them: and he said unto him, So shall thy . . ."

I don't know whether she said any more; the night seemed to swallow her words, and she was already on her way. I went back to the room and stared at the baby carriage. I fetched the official sheets for the coupons and started sticking them on. And the carriage stood just in front of me. It wasn't empty;

there was a blanket inside, a pillow and some baby clothes. When it has come to this, when a woman expecting her first child has to give away the baby carriage because the death sentence has been pronounced over her unborn child without cause, when that can happen the world can never be right again. You just can't restore the balance. And really there's no remedy left, except one: to clear up thoroughly—with fire.

I don't remember very much more about that night. We hadn't much energy left by the end of the day, at that stage of the war, and it's quite likely that I simply dropped off to sleep over those coupons. They got burned too in the fire, and you can imagine how much trouble that caused me later. I dare say I still heard the air raid warnings, but probably took them for something quite different. Why I didn't get up when it all started, that's something I don't know till this day. And then it all took the course which it had to take; I think you know what that course was.

Now it's almost dawn, sir, and I've just finished rereading this letter once more. Now I must end by thanking you very much for hearing my story out.

Yours sincerely,
Margarete Walker.

No, I did not know what had happened after that. I knew nothing at all about it.

Whether she, Frau Walker, surprised by the sirens and the British bombers (it was the very raid that is commemorated on the stone tablet to be found in the reconstructed Museum Library), saw fit to abandon all this, all her possessions, the house and herself to the alien fire, believing, perhaps, that one individual at least must crawl into the fiery furnace and take no thought for safety—or whether she was simply tired out, too tired to return to a world in which a mother has to part with her unborn baby's carriage—this question remains open, and I for one am not likely ever to find out the truth. I shall never ask anyone about it; one does not ask questions about such things. Besides, this letter and its message are sufficient in themselves.

Such is the world. Such is the monstrous face of Power. Such are the mauled and mangled lives of those who have passed through the great mincing machine of the age. And such is the infinitesimal, the marvelous possibility of man. One can hand over a piece of wrapping paper and conceal a message inside it. One can offer slices of cake to a couple of children. And, at the very end, one can take in a baby carriage—all these things one can do. An hour's trust and safety, a breath of peace. But no blossoming avenue of this world grants a radiance as bright as that light which penetrated through a chink in the door of the Jews' butcher, who stored up cubes of meat extract and often enough had nothing better to offer her customers than bits of tough beef full of bones and gristle.

[4]

SABINE TELEPHONED. NINE DAYS HAD PASSED SINCE OUR CONVERSA-tion that night and we'd hardly seen each other since: she'd been to Hanover on business and I'd only just been able to hand her Frau Walker's long letter before the train moved off. Now—soon after the end of our office hours—she called me up. From the voice alone I could tell that it wasn't any of the Sabines I knew.

"My father has written."

"Oh. I suppose he didn't mention Frau Walker?"

"He mentioned nothing else. You must come to see me. Soon. At once. Tonight. It's important."

I went. Sabine's father's letter lay on the table beside Frau Walker's letter. They lay on the table like omens, separate omens that will nevertheless combine, because one keeps watch over the other. Who will combine them?

"Everything after the first sheet," Sabine said.

"You read it to me."

"No." It was almost a shriek. "I can't. One can't read that kind of letter to *anyone*."

". . . and never thought, my dear, that I should ever have to tell you directly about those events. True, I always knew I mustn't depart from this life without leaving an account of them. But this account was to be kept locked up indefinitely, a testament, as it were. But I suppose I'd better tell you now what you don't know: that during the summer months of 1942 I returned for a few weeks to your immediate vicinity, so that in fact I saw you there once or more than once every day. So I know everything about your way of life in those days, even your way to school in that town. I was there before eight o'clock in the morning and soon after noon, when you went home for lunch. I know every dress you wore in those days. I saw you wear the embroidered blouse which I'd once brought back for your mother from Dalmatia, and I saw my child turn into a young lady, a little more so each day. I saw your face and the faces of the girl friends who went home with you. Sometimes I heard you laugh. Often enough I stood quite close to you, but I never yielded to the temptation to speak to you again. I was aware of the confusion this would bring into your life and your mother's life, and so I desisted, much as I should have liked you to know I was there. For homesickness was just beginning to consume me. There are twenty-four hours in the day, and in every one of those hours it can make itself felt. It's six o'clock in the morning, and Sabine is getting up. It's noon, and Sabine is starting her lunch. It's getting dark and Sabine will soon go to bed. It's nighttime and Sabine wakes up. It's the hour for prayer, and Sabine does not join me in prayer. I'm listening to music, and Sabine doesn't hear it. A tree is in leaf, and Sabine doesn't see it. That's how it was.

Like all of us, I had to get my meat ration at Frau Walker's; and during my last week in Germany I twice had the chance to talk to her after closing time. On the second of those two evenings I showed her the photographs I carried in my wallet.

This isn't the moment to speak about Frau Walker, or rather about the matters we discussed on those two occasions. She looked at your photographs; you can see how intently she looked at them from the fact that she recognized you in the hallway on your way out with Dr. S. (to whom I send my best wishes). There was a place for us all in her gaze.

Then came the third evening, my last in that town, it was the sixteenth of October—I remember the date because on the morning of the seventeenth I received the great news, the express letter from Sweden that informed me of the unexpected reprieve of which you know. I was staying with the G's., quite close to Walker, the butcher's. There was an air-raid alarm that night and at first I stayed in my room, as usual. If only out of consideration for the G's., I never made use of the shelter in the cellar of the house, and till then we'd got off lightly. But that night they meant business. I heard the bombs come down not many streets away and suddenly thought of the public shelter on the other side of the road. I hurried there without dressing, but turned back again on the stairs to get my overcoat. Often since I've had occasion to reflect how very different that night would have been if I hadn't gone back to get my coat. I dare say I should have reached the shelter unhurt and perhaps even got back safely to my room, for neither the shelter nor our house received a direct hit that night. As it was, I wore my coat and, on it, the yellow star; the air-raid warden in the shelter noticed it at once, at the entrance, and forbade me to come in. It was a bad moment, a moment I don't want to recall. As I turned back into the street I found it lit up by a great blaze, was met by smoke and the smell of burning, and decided to look for the fire—why, I don't know and shall never know. The anti-aircraft guns were in action and I heard the hum of foreign planes. I ran down the street and remember saying to myself, 'Of course!' when, turning the corner, I found that it was the Walkers' house that was blazing and pouring acrid smoke into the street. The top floor was on fire; the two lower ones, as far as one could see anything through the smoke, were still intact. But at the moment I came to the garden gate another bomb hit the house. I fell on my face and felt a violent blow on my chin; blood was trickling out of my mouth, but it didn't hurt, only my eyes smarted with the heat and smoke. You know I'm hardly an acrobat—but suddenly I was up on the window sill on the ground floor sitting room; all I know was that there was something I must save in the Walkers' house. The last blast had splintered the windowpanes. I saw—in a cloud of fire—I saw Frau Walker sitting at her table, called out to her but got no answer. I leaped into the room, rushed to the door and opened it, when more fire broke in from the hall. I seized her arm—she was half-unconscious—risked the five or six yards to the front door, found the key in the lock—thank heaven—managed to turn it and got her out. I was only slightly hurt, but the woman's face looked ghastly in the glow of the fire. Some fifty or sixty paces away—as far as I could drag her, for she could hardly be said to have walked—I laid her on a bench and covered her with my overcoat, having torn off part of her half-smouldering skirt just in time. The bench, I found, belonged to the next house but one; it was safe enough for the moment. I'd long ago made mental note of the fire alarm in our street and I found it quickly, broke the glass and heard the sirens begin to wail. All at once it struck me; on the overcoat covering Frau Walker there was that star, the yellow star. I hurried back and quickly ripped it off. Frau Walker opened her eyes; she recognized me now, smiled for a moment, but then said very softly and gravely, 'He has not accepted it.' 'Accepted what?' 'The burnt offering. God has not accepted it.'

Those were almost the last words I heard spoken in German, but I needn't tell you, Sabine, that I felt little desire to hear any others. The fire engine was on its way. They'd find the injured women; my work was done.

I returned to my lodgings. Early next morning the Swedish courier arrived—Dr. G. had directed him—and gave me the letter that meant I was saved."

"No regards to Frau Walker," I said, as I pushed the letter over to Sabine; "that's strange."

"Yes, it is strange. But I suppose formalities hardly apply in such a case."

[5]

TO CONCLUDE, THEN. BUT THIS IS ONE OF THOSE INGENUITIES OF life of which we say that they are both foolish and incomprehensible. A man goes on a journey for professional reasons, as he is sometimes obliged to do on account of an ancient manuscript he has never seen, and as he unpacks his briefcase at night in the hotel he happens to glance at a sheet of newspaper. At home he had taken a newspaper from the stack without looking, one of many newspapers mouldering in the junk room of the Walkers' house; now he is tired, distraught and only glad that he can bolt the door of his hotel bedroom and that his traveling flask of brandy isn't quite empty yet. So he spreads out the sheet of newspaper and lets his glance wander over the short advertisements column. "Walker," his eyes read, and he begins to take notice. "Walker" it is, no mistake.

And I read that Karl Walker, the butcher, announces the re-opening of his shop. I look for the date and see that the paper is seven months old. "High Quality Meat and Poultry. Specialists in Black Pudding," it says. And in the margin, curiously lost in that place, a Bible reference, II Moses 3:2. Like an afterthought added in haste, it looked on that page, or as if inserted in the wrong place by a careless printer. For what was a Bible reference doing here? You can understand the inclusion of a Bible reference in the obituary notice of a Christian, but what is the connection between black pudding and II Moses 3?

The reference: a librarian should know that the Moses story begins in the book of Exodus and, if he knows his Bible, he will remember that the third chapter relates how Moses was called. But what is the passage itself and what, if the reference is really not an accident, does it signify here?

It is a quarter to ten at night. Shall I trouble the hotel management for a Bible? I'm afraid they can provide anything rather than a Bible. I lift the receiver and ask the telephone exchange of the hotel to connect me with one of the parish offices in the town. It is Friday night (Frau Walker's evening, it occurs to me for a moment), and a quarter to ten, so it wouldn't be too importunate of me to telephone at this hour. The pastor will receive the call in his house, for he'll be working at his Sunday sermon at home, and that means his Bible won't be far away.

"What can I do for you?"

I state my name and my request. A Bible text is what I require.

"One moment, please." The pastor's voice is calm and betrays little astonishment. "Yes, here it is. The passage in question reads: '. . . and he looked, and, behold, the bush burned with fire, and the bush was not consumed.' "

"And the bush was not consumed." I understood; it was a question, long ago posed in silence, and an answer, slowly grasped.

The question: whether there is one who can balance the terrible guilt of the age against the wild self-immolation of a butcher's wife, against this readiness to crawl into the fiery furnace.

But one who could draw up this balance will say that he "desires not sacrifice," that he "delights not in burnt offering" nor in "the peace offerings of your fat beasts," but only in a broken spirit and a contrite heart. And would say— and this is the answer—that all of them, even he who shares the knowledge of it, Sabine, too, so curiously interwoven with it, and Sabine's father, who saved and was saved, have been retained for further service. True, in the burn on the woman's face that sign will remain, the sign that must not be interpreted otherwise than as a sign of love, of that love which maintains the world. . . .

"Is there anything else I can do?"

I'd forgotten that I still held the receiver in my hand. All I heard was a vague noise.

"I beg your pardon?"

"Is there anything else I can do?"

"Anything else? No. Nothing else. Thank you. Thank you very much. Good night."

Albrecht Goes 🕉 THE BOYCHIK

To Martin Buber—Teacher, Father, Friend

[1]

LEIB IS SCREAMING. WHEN HE HAD CLIMBED UP ON THE TRUCK right at the last moment, nimble as a cat, he kept silent. Leib —that was his name; at that time it was the others who yelled out to him: a man's voice with a shrill scream from up on the truck, and almost at the same moment from a distance of about a hundred feet a woman's voice from the path: "Leib!" Small and slender, twelve or thirteen years old, a little fellow whose black hair hung down over his forehead—that was Leib. He had tied the coat, Stefan's coat, around his head and shoulders, like the inner tube of a bicycle. The blue farmer's shirt came down over his hips, but because of the tightly fastened belt it looked like military clothing—little soldier Leib, wearing his summer uniform in the middle of the Ukrainian winter. Where the sidearm should have been there was a little spoon. The wintry light of the early afternoon fell on the little silver spoon. Only for a moment it gleamed and glistened; then the boy had disappeared into the back of the truck. Five men in uniform could be seen standing up there; they were wearing

143

winter overcoats, shakos and machine guns. You couldn't tell who else might be crouching or lying on the wooden beds; no one even saw the man who had called out this "Leib!"

"Aha, you've found your tongue again?" That was the voice of the one in drab who was standing on the upper foot-board and who could see into the truck from there. Then there was a pause, and then a count—triumphantly came the number "Seventeen." Seventeen—that was the number of captives; the boy Leib was the seventeenth one.

"Take off," said the one in drab, slamming the door to the cab up front. And then they drove into the forest of Berdichev, and for the seventeen up there it was a trip of no return.

At that time he was completely still, little Leib. But now, after twenty years—yes, exactly twenty years—now he's screaming. What should you do when someone is standing downstairs outside the door and unconsciously pushes on the doorbell with his arm or his overcoat, and there is a storm, and he does not hear the sound of the buzzer? Well, you have to get up in the middle of the night, open the window and yell down: "Please stand just half a step to the side, my contemporary, sir; why, you're waking up the whole house!" But nothing is accomplished here with a half-measure.

I don't know whether he'll stop screaming if I talk about him. I would not have said anything more about Stefan or of Matka. I am not for silence at any price, nor for talking at any price; I'm not for either one. But as for Stefan and Matka, considering many factors, I would have told myself, "Where are they better preserved than in the silent memory of one who, as long as he lives, keeps in himself a few breaths of their lives and thus changes a nameless death—how should I say it? —into a handful of gratefulness. . . . No, let's not be pompous—only this: that in his own life a person does a few things, or perhaps does not do them because for a year and a half in Vinnitsa a Jewish workman crossed his path a couple of times. I know a little about Stefan, and Matka is preserved in Stefan. But the boy, the boychik—"My little boychik" Stefan called him—he wants to come back to life again. Admittedly I can hardly describe him; I saw him only twice—on the evening before the black day and then at this moment of departure—and even then only from a distance; but description is one thing and invocation is something else.

It was pure chance—as one speaks of pure chance—that I arrived at the main entrance to our field clinic at that very moment on that turbulent day. The first half of the day we had been here and there at the various hospital wards. Just after the noonday meal I had gone into Building B, the surgery ward, and was scarcely done there; but of course one was never done. Wels, the little Franciscan friar, had tried to reach me by telephone and had told me about a dying soldier in the internal medicine ward (it was housed in the main building), and I wanted to get to him without delay; thus I was an eyewitness to this murderous kidnaping during the last two minutes. I say "murderous kidnaping" because I take no stock in euphemisms. I had heard the shot from a distance; even this shot was quite unusual; it was not customary to shoot in the area of our hospital. It had been, as I learned later, nothing more than a blank cartridge. The "mobilization leader"—or does one say "chief of operation"—the arch-rogue seemed to like that kind of surprise. Then, as I got closer I saw the truck, and on the path to the right two nurses and several civilians. One nurse was busy stuffing a handkerchief in the mouth of one of the women, but the cry "Leib" still came piercing through the crisp winter air. I went toward the entrance; Staff Doctor Jarisch, the oculist, stood in the doorway.

"What's going on here, Dr. Jarisch?" I asked.

Dr. Jarisch looked at me. It seemed as if he was about to start an explanation, but then there came only an "excuse me," with which he turned away. He walked five, six steps and vomited. What? What was that? I hesitated a moment; but because of the dying soldier to whom I had been called, I did not want to delay. I went into the building.

What had happened here? In the vestibule everything

seemed to be going according to daily routine. There were the
places for the telephone operators and for a couple of record
clerks, and the mail table where a new nurse, Ulrike, was supposed to be helping at the time. Her place was empty. Big gray
sacks were lying around unopened on the floor, at the side
there were at least two dozen little packages piled up (it was
December 20th—that was a rough time for the army post office;
the homeland remembers its fighting men). From the damaged
parcels came the fragrance of fir branches, the Spessart prov-
ince of Germany was penetrating the Ukraine, as were the
Black Forest, the Eifel, the Wester Forest ("Oh thou beautiful
Westerwald"), and also the smell of gingerbread and Christmas currant-cakes, the smell of love and labor, almond oil and
margarine.

"Switchboard . . . I'm calling Ward E. Staff Doctor Jessen
is on his way. . . . Give me Nurse Magda, please. . . . Zero
seven three two one." Those were the sounds of every hour of a
hospital day here; and they were not interrupted now.

On the left side of the outer office was the orderly-room,
barely protected from the noise of the corridor traffic. I looked
in through the little glass window; Sergeant Major Hirzel was
sitting at his desk looking at a sheet of paper, but, it seemed to
me, not really reading it. The seat across from him—it was for
the orderly-room private on duty—was empty, but on the stool
in front of the typewriter, with his face turned halfway to the
side, sat Dr. Wieland, our chief medical officer.

As usual, he was wearing his field blouse and long pants. But
the riding boots, which were supposed to emphasize his status
as an officer in the medical corps, were deeply repugnant to
him. "I tell you I'm a surgeon, not a gentleman rider," he
would say if he was questioned by some dashing military type.
But that didn't happen often. Now he was sitting on the stool
and staring into space. His pistol belt was lying on the typewriter and the two top buttons of the field blouse were open.
. . . Something must have happened. He wasn't faint or
white as a sheet like Staff Doctor Jarisch outside. Only now did
I remember his pallor. He didn't look like that, but . . . *what*

had happened? I considered the possibility of simply asking, but then it seemed rather untactful of me to step in right now. I turned around, determined to make my visit to the ward right away. The medical record clerks didn't look up from their work; but then it was the private at the telephone switchboard who must have sensed my questioning glance. He turned to me and said: "They picked up Stefan."

[2]

I'LL HAVE TO RELATE HOW WE CAME UPON STEFAN. WE CAME upon Stefan because we needed him, and consequently we considered it a stroke of luck that we had come upon him. In July '42, when conditions were stabilized here and the main line of battle ran a thousand kilometers further to the east, the four buildings of an agricultural academy had been turned over to us for our field clinic. The commandant made several tours with his administrative assistants through the whole compound. He belonged at that time to a field hospital, and, remembering the misery of his first Russian winter, he finally decided with some concern, "It's all a question of heat. We'll have to find someone who understands this central heating system. It is simple and intricate at the same time, like most things here. And somebody who doesn't mind the miserable crawling that might be necessary—that's really a labyrinth there, gentlemen—I mean an expert welder who has a sensitive ear where something is frozen up—and it'll freeze here—and I still remember well that stinking mess in Poltava . . . if we find somebody, all right; if we don't, good night! Ehni, take whatever you want from the canteen, take cigarettes, vodka, chocolate, cigarette lighters—but dig up a man for us! Take Marulla along; she'll interpret up a storm for you—and she's pretty too. Yeah, yeah, don't laugh—an attraction for the stoker, when he comes, *if* he comes. . . ."

Paymaster Ehni had been snooping around and keeping his

ears open here and there. It was already the beginning of September; we couldn't wait much longer, for winter could come early. Finally a lead was found—the Jew knows, he knows his way around. Good. And where does the man live? In such and such a place. Don't lose any time. Ehni set out on foot and not exactly in broad daylight; Marulla went along, but what good is an interpreter if the guy doesn't want to understand? My God, how these chosen ones can keep quiet. . . . The lies we've been told about Jewish hair-splitting and such. . . . Reality is different, *this* reality at least. And as for my bait— vodka, cigarettes—the man didn't even look at them. They just stood there—the three of them—in the room; the conversation wouldn't get off the ground. A dark room, dark shadows on the man's face. "But you are familiar with such systems, aren't you?" There, behind the second door, suddenly a child's voice—and right after it a woman's whisper. Sh! Sh! thought Ehni, so that's international. And then, turning to Marulla and speaking quickly: "Ask him if he doesn't want some chocolate for his children. . . ." At the word "children" the man's face twitched—only for an instant—; that happened not when Marulla translated, but even as Ehni asked the question. Aha, then he understands more than one might think, or at least more than he let on before. Well, then more directly: "Couldn't you at least come and tell one of our men about the system?" Ehni was thinking of Corporal Raible; he was no furnace expert, but a quick-witted fellow. And he thought: If I can get this man in our building once, maybe he'll stay. "Come."

"When?"

Right away, thought Ehni, right now. Strike the iron while it's hot.

"Right now?"

He wanted to add a third bar of chocolate to the two already on the table, but again there was resistance on the dark, narrow face and something was said almost soundlessly to Marulla —and Marulla interpreted: "He said that was enough; he doesn't want any more."

And then they went, at first side by side; but over there in the compound area on the other side of the Bug River, Ehni stayed a couple of steps behind the two. "We'd better go to the Chief right away; maybe the Chief will bring it off."

[3]

"SENIOR STAFF DOCTOR" WAS HIS TITLE IN THE MILITARY HIER-archy, but to Dr. Wieland this was of no consequence. Other outfits called their commanders "the old man"; but it would not have occurred to any of us to speak of "the old man." "The Chief" was enough of a title, and it still applied to the officers' mess at midnight when this man of vitality tapped out a song with all ten fingers on the table: "A guy ought to be able to play the piano. If you play the piano you have good luck with women. . . ."[1] He was somebody, and he knew he was some-body, and anyone who had to deal with him soon knew it too. That was true in the clinic in Hamburg, and it was true now. The conquering type, then? Maybe. But whoever sees the paths which precede victory; who sees the struggle?

On this very day he had received news from home that greatly disturbed him. In the code language that was custom-ary then when people wanted to tell the truth, his wife had informed him that on Green Shrub Road[2] there had been unexpected commotion because of the sudden departure of Dr. S. M. From this the recipient of the letter deduced that a Jewish specialist in internal medicine had been "picked up" on Red Tree Highway, and that therefore the neighborhood had been aroused about this action of the Gestapo after all.

Dr. M. . . . They had known each other for two or three years only through telephone contacts; such a situation is com-mon enough in a large city among professional colleagues.

[1] Lyrics of a German hit song of the 'twenties.—Eds.
[2] Grünensträucherweg instead of Rothenbaumchaussee, a street in Ham-burg.—Eds.

Then there had been a few direct meetings and several personal conversations; finally something like friendship had come about. Dr. M. had lived a completly secluded life for a long time prior to 1933; he was never seen at the theater or at any social affair. "Oh, there's nothing to that," he would say whenever anyone called attention to this life of strict asceticism. "Excuse me"—this "Excuse me" came up often in his conversation; it was a request he expressed rather gaily—"you have to have your tools within reach." He was always on the job; a half hour of music in the evening was all the recreation he allowed himself. His practice, a rather good practice in internal medicine, had not suffered much loss at first even in the year after the Nazis' seizure of power. Dr. M. had been a combat officer in the First World War; that protected him for a while from the interference of the hoodlums. A detail about his consultations with his patients was gossiped about—he had the habit of asking his patients to undress completely even when they came to him about sinus trouble or a swollen knee. Naturally, with the help of the scandal sheets this procedure netted him the usual insinuations. But the patients did have their own opinion about this. "It was as if somebody else were looking at you"—Doctor Wieland remembered this comment of a patient who had been referred to him by Dr. M. for further treatment. This patient was the legal counsel of a vulcanizing factory, not a towheaded poet. What led him to speak of God the Father under such circumstances? During a medical consultation the two doctors had quite by chance also touched upon this habit of Dr. M. "Oh, that!" said the internist almost shyly, "there's nothing to that. It's just—well, maybe that will make me think of something." God knows, he *had* thought of something. When you saw him you knew what was meant . . . you understood what it means: a doctor. And now he had "left town." Dr. M. was out of town for the time being.

The senior staff doctor had had coffee brought into his office next to the operating room; it was approaching six o'clock. "If possible, no interruption for half an hour, please." Now this half hour was up, and Lemmen, the operating room assistant, who knew how to keep watch over the Chief's rest periods like a Cerberus, announced the presence of paymaster Ehni.

"Dr. Wieland, sir, I've brought you a stoker!"

"Ehni! Boy, I'll put your name in for the Cross of Merit if that man is worth anything. Bring him here!"

Ehni quickly said what was necessary, and then the Ukrainian was called in with Marulla.

"You understand German?"

"A little."

"And I know a little Russian. O.K. *Khorosho.*"

"*Khorosho.*"

"Do you have any children?"

"A boy."

"I have a boy too. Good. *Khorosho.*"

And the man spoken to responded, even though a bit hesitantly and quite softly: "*Khorosho.*"

Then there was a pause. Suddenly the Chief said: "Please, Paymaster Ehni, go with the interpreter to the head nurse and clear up that business with the washwomen. . . ."

That was pure nonsense. There was no business with the Ukrainian washwomen that needed clearing up. But Ehni understood right away that the Chief wanted the interpreter out of the room without it appearing obvious: two ears less for what would be discussed.

"Your name is Stefan."

"No, Chief, Sir, my name is . . ."

"Listen to what I'm telling you: Your name is Stefan." Stefan? Stefan: That was the name written across this day. That was Dr. M.'s name. Stefan must endure. "Here you have food, pay, clothing. You will keep our heating system in order as soon as winter arrives. And there'll be plenty to do otherwise. Where you come from—that's nobody's business. You'll keep your mouth shut. Do you understand? Mouth shut. Mouth shut."

"I understand. Mouth shut. Name is Stefan. Mouth shut."

"Good, Stefan. *Khorosho*. Paymaster Ehni will tell you everything else. Wait for him here, please—I have things to do."

When Ehni came back, Stefan was taken over in proper form. There was no longer any talk about a temporary arrangement. Dr. Wieland had immediately made Stefan a part of the community of the field clinic. So that's the way it's done, thought Paymaster Ehni. And he thought: He's a whiz, the Chief—a real wizard.

[4]

"WE'LL HAVE TO GET STEFAN" BECAME A REGULAR SLOGAN IN the building. Fortunately winter took its time in coming, but even without his duties as stoker, Stefan was no longer without work even a day. He could—well, what *couldn't* he do? He was a plumber, an electrician, a glazier, a carpenter. But he was also a painter when necessary, and even a mason when nobody else was available. At the nursing stations, in the pharmacy, in the billets, in the kitchen—Stefan was everywhere.

Or maybe he wasn't everywhere. At least not everywhere in the same way. He had the scent not of an animal but of a human being who knows he is in danger. In a very short time he knew all of us and who was favorably inclined toward him and who was not. As one would expect, Ehni had kept well the secret of his origin if only as a matter of self-protection. One is, of course, powerless against suspicions. It was lucky that Stefan's appearance supported no dangerous surmise. Furthermore, he had taken that "mouth shut" to heart, with the result that no one really had a chance to be concerned with Stefan as a person. In this building he was an instrument, a useful instrument. You would call him, explain a wish; he would listen —neither sullenly nor intently. You could never determine completely how much he understood of what you said to him by way of elucidation. He set to work in silence; it was seldom that he accepted any assistance. "You've done a good job, Stefan," people used to say when the work was done. But even then he was silent, and his big dark eyes did not smile.

Two moments are vividly present to me. Soon after his arrival in our building I had to make use of his assistance—there was a loose electrical connection to be fixed in my room. I possessed at that time a little protective silver shield, a kind of amulet, that hung on the wall next to my desk. A Hebrew word had been engraved into the shield. It was God's first question in this world, that "Where art thou?" from the book of Genesis. In the mysteriously telescoping root language of the Old Testament these three words became *one* word, and their sound moves past like an arrow: *ayekkah.*

I kept on writing at my desk while Stefan was working and noted only how he brushed the little shield with a very quick, timid movement. I said not a word, and Stefan gave no sign of having understood a word. But four or five days later, when we met in the hallway, he said something he had never said before: "Good evening, Chaplain." Maybe—it's quite possible—there was really nothing special in this greeting; but maybe it was also an answer to this holy *ayekkah:* his answer.

And then—that was a year later—our paths crossed outside between the wards. Then there was a little conversation, and he even smiled for a moment. The officials who had recently been attached to our unit had passed by us, and I had said: "New paymaster, new pharmacist. You belong to the old guard already, Stefan."

"Old guard," he repeated, and while he repeated it, it was not clear to me whether he knew the expression, but then came his smile; it came and disappeared, and then he said: "Old guard . . . scrap iron."

[5]

THE ATMOSPHERE OF A BUILDING—IS THERE SUCH A THING? OR IS
here where uniforms are worn every building like the other,
just as good, just as bad? Definitely not. The commander of a
unit can to no small extent determine two elements: concern
and discretion. He cannot convert the razor-sharp types you
find on duty everywhere to humanitarianism; he cannot stuff
the mouths of professional gossips. But he can see to it that
these two types do not set the tone. A military clinic in the
fourth year of war—well, that is not exactly a "Club for the
High-Minded," and there simply is not enough time for any
birthday celebrations, to give just one example. But concern is
more than cake and coffee. The birth of a child back home, a
death, loss in an air raid—such things were shared mutually;
we were concerned about one another. An audience with the
Chief and a soul-searching—no, not that. It was more likely that
Dr. Wieland, to whom the sergeant major had reported a
special case, would, without any further questions, grab the
nearest telephone. Then there was a vociferous conversation
with the air base commander: Thus and thus—and when does
the next plane take off? . . . And then: Is the courier plane
there mainly for the administrative officer's cans of sunflower oil
and not just as much for Corporal Malten—"a fine assistant in
my operating room"; this was said with almost threatening emphasis—Malten, "M" as in Martha, "A" as in . . . certainly,
the one who has to see about the rubble heap in Essen which up
to now has been his home . . . thank you . . . good morning.
Whereupon he would plod over to the operating room, and as
he put on his white coat, he would say to the unsuspecting
corporal, "You take off at two o'clock, Malten; get your papers
ready . . . and don't fall down . . . 'bye." So much for that;
and now the second factor—discretion. It wasn't otherwise and
could not be any other way—in a building with seventy, eighty
people, not even including the patients, there was enough that
was difficult and dismal in cases of drunkenness and insubordi-

nation, mésalliances, divorces, attempted suicides. The rule of the house was: no palaver, and certainly no compositions, no reports or paper wars. Five sentences if possible. And better still: mouth shut.

We didn't talk about Stefan either. He was there; he was part of the furniture. He wore the medical corpsman's field jacket, and one day even the field cap. You would sometimes find him in the evening with the mess tin on his belt. No one in the kitchen had asked: Why are you taking a second helping of soup? Why vegetables again? No one asked: Where are you going? Silence is silence, we might have thought. But perhaps we thought:What I don't know won't hurt me. Thus I would hardly have learned the little story about the spoon if this time Paymaster Ehni had not wanted to have, so it seemed to me, at least one confidant, and perhaps also something like absolution.

It must have been late summer 1943; Stefan had now been with our outfit a whole year. At that time we were just having our chess playing season. On Sundays after eating there were a few games which we called rather grandiloquently our "tournament." Right at that time Pharmacist Jablonski, an Austrian, transferred into our unit. "I'm from Spittal, I'll have you know; you gentlemen surely know the late Rosegger." [3] The gentlemen did not know the late Rosegger, or at least only a few did, but Jablonski from Spittal was welcome anyway. It was he who right at the first or second noonday meal turned the conversation toward chess. As possibly interested parties, Staff Doctor Jessen, Paymaster Ehni and I were named, and he asked right away whether he might not challenge us; he said "challenge," if the gentlemen had nothing against it, preferably all three at the same time and simultaneously. . . . Oh, yes, the day after tomorrow, if it suited the gentlemen then. I laughed at the nonchalant charm with which he put across his point. But after the meal Jessen and Ehni took me aside: "He's

[3] Peter Rosegger (1843–1918), Austrian novelist, poet, and dramatist who frequently wrote in the dialect of the Steiermark, his Styrian homeland.— Eds.

really got the big-head, this *Ostmärker*," said Ehni, and
Jessen said: "Such arrogance ought at least to cost something.
Two bottles of red wine."

"Two bottles if he loses one game; four, if he loses two games.
And four bottles from us if he wins—justice demands it."
Whereupon Jablonski, when the wager was announced to him
at supper: "Oh sure, just as the comrades wish." I did not like
the appellation *"Ostmärker."* I stuck to *"Österreicher,"* [4] and
in doing so thought more of Grillparzer and Trakl [5] than of
Rosegger. . . .

I had offered my little warning right at the beginning when
there was still time: "Gentlemen, let me warn you about hasty
actions. Our bottles are as good as gone. If a guy comes from
Spittal, doesn't know us at all, and makes that kind of offer—I
tell you: He must be infernally sure of himself."

"So what," said Jessen.

Well, I was right; we lost, all three of us—he beat the pants
off us. In two short hours the whole thing was over. We packed
up our pretty little folding chess sets. "We'll break the necks of
those four bottles together, of course," said champion Jablonski, "but please . . . not a word . . . my pleasure."

Paymaster Ehni stayed there; I noticed that he wanted to get
something off his chest.

"We recently got some silver spoons from the effects of a patient. The man, a sergeant, had in his pack, and well wrapped
up, a whole case of them, Russian-made, quite old, silver
spoons, you know—dessert spoons . . . or, rather, a little
larger, kind of small tablespoons with a very interesting pat-
tern on the handle—a dozen. 'Liberated' merchandise, naturally. The man fell into a coma right after he arrived and died
on the same day. We could not bring ourselves to send home

---

4 *Ostmärker:* Nazi terminology for Austrian, as opposed to *Österreicher,*
the normal German word.—Eds.

5 Franz Grillparzer, Austrian dramatist, 1791–1872. Georg Trakl, Austrian
poet, 1887–1914.—Eds.

the case he had dragged along from heaven knows where along with his other things . . . and I didn't want to register it either. I now intend using them in the officer's club. The spoons must have been lying a long time in some damp place; they were thoroughly tarnished. I couldn't give them to the women who clean up in the kitchen, which left only Stefan. You know, Stefan knows everything and does everything. In three days he had them polished bright. I asked: 'What would you like to have, Stefan? Chocolate?'

" 'No,' he said, 'not chocolate.'

" 'What then?'

" 'A little spoon, sir.'

"I said, 'But that won't do. What are you thinking of? You can't show up down there with the silver spoon. What will people think?'

" 'Not . . . Not . . . '

" 'Do you want to take it to your wife?'

" 'For the boychik, sir, for the boychik.'

"And listen, reverend, I did it. I gave him one of those spoons. He can speak German pretty well now, but when his feelings get the best of him, he speaks Russian again. He kept saying, '*Spassivo*,' and when he left, he kissed my hand. What do you think?"

"Good, Ehni, good. You're taking care of balance in the world. What's the use in all this plundering and arson, this gobbling up of territories? So that Stefan, Jr., the little one, will get a silver spoon."

[6]

STALINGRAD, ELBRUS, SEVASTOPOL, EL ALAMEIN—THAT WAS THE year 1943; that was it—but then it was also the fall of Mussolini, the landing of the enemy in Africa. But for us it meant lung wounds, leg amputations, first and second degree burns, typhoid fever over and over again. . . . The big air raid on Hamburg in the middle of the year had hit our Chief, too—his clinic was destroyed—and when the calendar read November, the number of our unit who had not yet been affected was smaller than the number who had. Now the air travel time for the arrival of casualties was ominously short; by the time of the first Advent Sunday the neighboring town of Zhitomir was no longer outside the danger zone. Orders were already reaching us to prepare to evacuate the clinic, then strict orders revoked them. . . . In the areas where catchwords were in vogue the idea was expressed by optimists and pessimists alike, even though in contrasting tones: Well, with God's help we'll be on the move right on Christmas Day, or in Poland, in Hungary, in Austria . . . those are nice places, too.

But right along with this, the administrative machinery kept operating—a familiar phenomenon. New beds arrived; a special station for orthopedic surgery was to be "ready for use by December 15th"; large amounts of highly perishable vaccine were arriving in the pharmacy. Just before the bitter cold set in, Stefan had put lights in the whole labyrinth of his heating system. And then there were new assignees to our outfit, as if things would go on here for a long time. Two nurses were sent to us from the Minsk area. When the teletyped orders came, the Chief matter-of-factly gave us their names—Nurse Else and Nurse Ulrike. Nurse Else—there were already two by that name here; she would probably have to be called Else 3; as for Nurse Ulrike—and this we heard rather soon, even before her arrival—she was an unusual case: from Mecklenburg and of noble birth—that was almost disconcerting in a Westphalian nursing staff—peasant Westphalians with a supplement of homespun Swabians. She had become a widow while still young and had had some university training. The nurses began to be concerned about their positions. The head nurse promised to shunt her off to some other respectable job unless we were terribly shorthanded here. "We'll make her postmistress—that's a pretty nice job for a start."

"Nurse Ulrike looks like somebody from the Prince of Homburg's[6] entourage," reported Staff Doctor Jessen at the table. He was the doctor in charge of the nursing staff; she had been taken to him right after her arrival. "From Mecklenburg and of the nobility?" people asked—and then: "A Naziette, eh?" "Nazi? We didn't get that far in the first conversation. I would say no." And after a pause, more definitely now: "No. A confirmed Christian, I would say."

I had greeted Nurse Ulrike in the hallway on the third or fourth day; there was only enough time for a handshake, but I thought right away: A character from a Kleist drama—Jessen had characterized her pretty well. Then came the worship service of the fourth Sunday of Advent; Nurse Ulrike was there, and without looking up she listened with such concentration that the speaker had the feeling he was addressing this one listener alone. At that time you were often the preacher, organist and sexton all at once. When I was straightening up the room after the service, she stayed and helped me; that's when our first conversation came about. We even had some acquaintances in common—it's a small world—and then the discussion turned, I don't know how, to connections with the Quakers of Holland—connections which, of course, were now harshly broken off. This alone sufficed as a legitimate identification for each other. With some hesitancy I asked her about her husband. Yes, he had lost his life at Minsk in July of 1942; the official report read "shot by partisans." "I have reason to doubt this official report, and still more to keep quiet about my own opinion. Is that enough?" This "Is that enough?" was really more like "Lieutenant so-and-so" or "Baroness von———" than just "Red Cross Nurse Ulrike." And I said, "Yes, that's enough, nurse." Then on the way back, in a lighter tone, I asked whether she had been able to get halfway settled in the new house. . . . Under the circumstances you really didn't know whether it was worth it or not. In any case, as I told her,

[6] A reference to a play by Heinrich von Kleist (1777–1811) in which the leading characters are of the North German nobility.—Eds.

for almost any wish the magic words here were "See Stefan." "Oh, is that the electrician? I know him already." "Stefan is the stoker. You're most likely to find him in the mornings in the basement."

"Tell me—excuse the silly question—is he a Jew?"

"What do you mean?"

"I . . . we had up there . . . I mean, we had this type up there in Minsk. Is this Stefan. . . ?" She saw my face. "Or—is that a military secret?"

"Yes. A military secret. And as a military secret: Yes."

[7]

THAT "YES" WAS CARELESS. OR AT LEAST IRREGULAR. I WANTED TO match confidence with confidence; all right. And then, too, I really owed secrecy only to myself, but every word—isn't it true?—is one word too many.

I couldn't get it off my mind, and Klaus, my *frater catholicus,* noticed my confusion right away when we met in the officers' club that afternoon. We stood around awhile, expecting the chief medical officer, who was overdue.

"Out of sorts?" asked Klaus.

"Aw, not particularly. Only—a guy ought to carry around a lock for his mouth—like Papageno."

Klaus didn't get to continue the conversation; the Chief walked in. He had a note in his hand which he held out in front of himself like an alien object while he told us about its contents. "Pre-Christmas visit. They've planned a little something. A *Kreisleiter* from Franconia is coming and wants to distribute some Christmas presents. This afternoon." He folded the paper and looked over at me: "Presents and donations. . . . Reverend, that's your department. I can imagine that you don't have much taste for that kind of golden guy . . . but you'll have to do the honors. You or Klaus. Flip a coin over it."

"Me . . . a *Kreisleiter* . . . no. When that Nazi organ grinder starts in with 'Unsa Fü'a' [7], then I'll get rough."

"I'm giving you an official order not to get rough."

"Yessir, Senior Staff Doctor, sir . . . do the honors. Official order not to get rough." I repeated the orders according to regulations. Our little clique grinned all around, more good-naturedly than gloatingly. We all had a roguish gleam in our eyes; as far as I was concerned, it was a rather pitiful rogue.

Klaus, however, took note of it and quickly saved himself: "Franconia? Then you two can talk Swabian together. That's your domain. If they send a Westphalian to us next time, then I'll handle him."

I steeled myself for the worst, and, as almost always when you brace yourself for the worst, it came off better than expected . . . at least at first. The Nazi peacock was so taken aback by having to put up with a chaplain to accompany him in place of the chief medical officer—who, I had to say, was unavoidably detained (he really was, for an operation was scheduled)—that he couldn't say anything but "Well, all right then . . . let's get started right away." And so we started; a small detail—three enlisted men and three nurses—were assigned to me. The *Kreisleiter* had brought two men as gift-bearers. We were spared the 'Hohe Nacht der klaren Sterne," and when a nurse in all seriousness suggested "O du fröhliche" [8]—*sancta simplicitas!*—I shook my head hard. All right, no carols. Instead of that, first in the large hall and then in two other rooms there was a speech from the guest—short and bad. The whole spook-language started up—there was the "home front" and the "final victory," the "tightly fastened helmet" and "Our Führer" ("Unsa Fü'a"), the WHW and the NSV. [9] ("N.S. wee-wee," said a patient next to me; I put my finger to my mouth and thus did my little bit toward the success of the ceremony.) Then came the baskets, which looked

[7] A vulgarly pompous version of *Unser Führer*—"our leader."—Eds.

[8] Words to popular German Christmas carols.—Eds.

[9] The initials stand for Winter Relief Fund and National Socialist Welfare Organization.—Eds.

rather respectable—sweaters and wool vests, wine, cognac and even champagne, sausages, little hams, tin cans of all sorts, and Christmas currant-cakes. The patients were happy. I helped with the distribution. Actually, I believe it would have all come off rather tolerably if the hapless NCO corpsman hadn't had a bright idea at the very last moment. The *Kreisleiter* had mentioned his headquarters—a little town in Franconia. A funny name, the NCO thought, and then: Why, I've already heard that place name today—or did I read it? But where? On a patient's record, of course . . . right; it was the seriously wounded man over there, the double amputee . . . shouldn't we . . . but we did hang a "No admittance" sign on the door . . . but just for a moment . . . a greeting from his hometown . . . all right, I'll ask if the *Kreisleiter* himself wouldn't like to speak to a badly wounded countryman. . . . "Why, of course—why, right away."

We went in; not the whole entourage, only four or five of us. The NCO corpsman spoke very softly—a slight hint for the official—and the Nazi peacock seemed to understand the warning; he too began very politely. But suddenly the editorials got to him—there came "Ivan," after him, the "Bolshevistic subhumans," and then the "great retaliatory attack." The minute I saw the patient (whom I hadn't seen before), I got quite worried. That can't end well, I said to myself. He was a man nearer to forty than thirty—in civilian life? . . . difficult to say—maybe an engineer or businessman in some technical field. You could see—if you had learned to pay attention to such things—that his whole being was defiance. There was not the slightest tinge of a smile at the greeting. But then—who smiles with two stumps? . . . But this was not weariness; it was resistance. He kept his eyes closed during the *Kreisleiter's* rodomontades. "Stop that!" I wanted to say—I should have said it—but then, the right thing always goes unsaid. The patient—was he asleep maybe? No, he wasn't asleep at all. And then, when the *Kreisleiter* paused, it finally came. "Not Ivan—*you!*" And then again—every word seemed an effort to him,

and his pointing finger had to help him along, but it was absolutely clear what he wanted to say. And then he said it too:
"Not Ivan's fault—yours!"

The *Kreisleiter*, confused by this rejection contrary to the
program, turned halfway around, looking for witnesses to his
innocence. "Me? Me? Do I look like a leg butcher?" He sig-
naled to the man with him and took a bottle of champagne out
of the basket. "Here. All right, then. Champagne. Booty from
the French. First class. And as for your legs . . . buddy, they'll
make you fine artificial limbs . . . medical technology in this
day and age. . . ." The words stumbled over each other now.
The patient left his eyes open this time. They didn't look at
the gift. They rested in urgent seriousness on the face of the
man who was talking to him. They didn't ask—they answered.
For the third time now it came, this time without a word—
only a little shaking of his head and the pointing finger. And
then, nothing more.

Something like a tainted, sterile stillness had settled over the
room. I didn't look at the *Kreisleiter*. I knew he was being
stared at enough. For a short moment it occurred to me: He is,
even though uninvited, our guest. How far does hospitality go?
Should I come to his aid? Should I build a bridge? But then:
No. There's no help here. God's mills. . . .

"Heil Hitler!" said the man with the gold bars on his uniform. He didn't say it bluntly or loudly. It was his refuge . . .
his credo, his confession and absolution, all in one. Then he
made for the door, but turned around again to the man nearest to him: "Give the NCO this basket for further distribution." Outside he wiped his brow with his handkerchief; the
corners of his mouth twitched. "Anything else to do?"

"Maybe in Ward 8," said the NCO corpsman.

We went in; there was attentive silence and then the greeting. The *Kreisleiter* went up to a table in the middle of a
room. He stopped behind the table. "I have instructions
to . . ." he started, and then came two or three more sentences. The spring had broken. The watch would run a few

seconds if you shook it . . . but it stopped. *"Rien ne va plus."* Where do people say that? Oh yes, in a gambling casino. The men accompanying the official distributed gifts. They essayed a kind of cheerfulness; it was terribly fake, this cheerfulness, but it was almost merciful. Then the basket was empty and they went outside in the hallway. There was nothing more but the blind salute, which at that time they called "the German salute"—the half-lifted hand and an unarticulated rasp. The ceremony of the marionettes. (But you *play* with marionettes. This here, the whole thing, was not play.) And then, without any further word of parting: "Where is my car?"

The driver, who had helped with the distribution, rushed to get to the exit quicker than his boss so he could drive up immediately. The *Kreisleiter* got in and they drove away. He stared straight ahead. *Finis.*

I—should I go back into the building once more? Is this a situation that needs a consoling word? Can a word solve anything here? No. Not a word now. Tomorrow maybe, or perhaps this evening. But not now. Every word is one word too much.

I thought of the man who had just fled, thought of him without any triumph. How long will things continue like that? Another year? Longer? Hardly longer. Then the credo of today will only be a rat's whisper. And those who believed it, will they begin again? Will they comprehend the incomprehensible? The man with his stumps—if he survives now, he'll get on his feet again. In that he was right, that consoler from Franconia. But as for him and the others—who will help them to their feet?

[8]

AND WHERE DO WE GO NOW? LATE AFTERNOON ON THE FOURTH Sunday of Advent—that could mean "Bach, Christmas Oratorio." "Jauchzet, frohlocket, auf, preiset die Tage. . . ." ["Be glad, rejoice, praise the days . . ."] Well, as far as rejoicing is concerned . . . yet: different air for an hour. Perhaps a wintry scene, a few steps on the iced-over Bug, a glance at something indestructible, at icicles on the weeping willows over there? No, better still: a human scene. I hadn't been to Old Vinnitsa in a long time; I hadn't gone to the Russian church for at least a year. It was located halfway up the hill over there on the other side of the Bug. The way went through the winding alleys of the old city. To be sure, it was hardly advisable for a German soldier to walk there alone, and most certainly not in the dark. But right now, maybe just for a half hour, it would be all right.

The beautiful church was locked, but the tiny little shops near it were there as always; sunflower seeds and dried mushrooms lay on a dusty-gray dish. Patched bicycle inner tubes were hanging on a pole; next to it fish nets and fishing lines. In another display you could see cornbread and dry greenish cheese. I couldn't help feeling that this "almost nothing" was more depressing than nothing at all, and the shadowy figures that scurried by were signs of an extinguished world. Resistance, danger from partisans? It didn't look that way anymore. This silent *nichevo*—that was the last station, the last chapter, expressed in our hospital tone of voice: the final stage. Why didn't I turn right around?

Suddenly in a black window a glance intended for me: Stefan. Here, then, is where Stefan lives. I sense, physically I sense, my eyes sending out their light, sending a greeting, begging for a greeting in return; but the man at the window doesn't reveal with any movement whatever that he knows me. "Mouth shut"—that's what he had been told, and Stefan repeated it to himself. I'm leaving;—if he had only greeted me! I'll walk a little farther toward the slope from where one can see the Bug.

And now, finally out in the open, something approaching joy did come upon me forcefully—intimacy in a strange place.

It is not only the white wintry sky, powerful and bright as in my fatherland over there, but also that other thing in whose indestructibility I believe—*shirokaya natura,* the little mother. Tolstoi's Cobbler Martin and his guest,[10] today and evermore.

It was too cold to sit down anywhere; so I walked back and forth up there—in a strange way both preoccupied and freed from care. I forgot that it turns dark here without any transition. And it did get dark. I must go back. Back by the same road. I want to see where Stefan lives once more without being observed—just from a distance. Now I realize it: Even if our departure from here should be delayed by one or two weeks, all of this here is our farewell. Farewell and (that was certain) farewell forever. If we should survive all this, even if one day we should get to Paris, to Amsterdam, to Rome, or wherever— to this place we would never return.

There was the alley. Stefan's cottage was almost in the dark; there were no real streets here, only nooks and crannies. But suddenly I was aware that someone was huddling at my side. Not Stefan, but—and that was recognizable right away—the miniature edition of Stefan, slender and dark and nimble. It was the boychik. I knew it before Stefan's name was uttered. He stepped right up close to me and began talking rapidly in his own language. I said the phrases we had learned to put across that we understood nothing, but he kept right on unperturbed in his speech in words and signs. Suddenly there came a word I understood—"Hanukah." Yes, Hanukah, Israel's Festival of Light—the festival of the concealed light of creation—it was about to be celebrated as well as our Christmas. And along with this there was a gesture that I should understand—his hands (what distinguished hands the little fellow had!) formed something long and narrow in the air. He wanted something from me—that much I grasped; but what could he want? Suddenly he disappeared, and immediately thereafter he was standing there again; now he took matches out of his pocket— our matches; I noticed it and had to laugh. But why shouldn't

[10] From Tolstoi's story *Where Love Is, God Is* (1885).—Eds.

Soldier Stefan buy canteen goods too? He struck a match, and then his left hand again formed—a candle. I knew now—he wanted a candle from me for the Festival of Hanukah.

Candles had become rather scarce with us too. I carried three or four in my luggage; I didn't want to touch this supply. Besides this I still had one pre-war yellow beeswax candle. All right, then. I nodded: a candle for you—give it to Stefan—for Hanukah.

He had understood me and smiled. Stefan's smile. No—there was here only the dark edge of Stefan's smile—Israel the Eternal. Inside it was the smile of a child—open and weightless. He was beautiful, the little fellow—beautiful in such a way that it was breathtaking. Terribly beautiful, we say now and then, and in saying so we aren't wrong. He took the hand I offered him only for a moment. Then he walked the few steps back to the cottage. At the doorway he stopped and raised the palms of both hands to eye level. It was the blessing of Jacob in the form of a boy.

After he disappeared I kept standing there. It was certain: Stefan himself would not appear at the window once more. But this boy—I reflected on the little one once more. Now he'll give a report to his father, to his mother—to his mother whom I had never seen face to face, in all that time not even once. Suddenly I was weary of the whole game of hide-and-seek. Even the name didn't suit me anymore, this Stefan deception that we had invented for his protection—for his or for our protection? I gave in to my feelings; I repeated to myself the name with which I had on occasion just to myself addressed the big-eyed slender man with the closed mouth of silence: Kafka, Prince Kafka. Well, then, a candle for the little Kafka—a candle for Hanukah.

[9]

I DIDN'T SEE THE CHIEF UNTIL I ENTERED THE OFFICERS' CLUB. I reported in and gave an account of my mission—should I say, the mission that failed? Naturally he had already heard a few details. I was very glad that he didn't say "Serves him right," but instead acknowledged my report with a short "Hm." At dinner we talked about the deactivation of the clinic; during the day the most recent orders from headquarters included specific deadlines. They were applicable to our unit with certain conditions; the chain of command, that sacrosanct part of every war machine, had fallen into confusion. The Chief was not very talkative that evening, and when he was called to the telephone toward the end of the meal, his face flushed with indignation. "Will you gentlemen stay here, please?" he said as he left the room. After ten minutes he returned and told us that another large group of wounded would arrive tomorrow by air—a hundred or more patients, he couldn't find out exactly how many. The army headquarters doctor had roared on the phone. "I told him we had orders to reduce personnel and be prepared to abandon this place within twenty-four hours. Then he said he didn't give a hoot about what those jackasses in Rovno ordered. Gentlemen, I talked myself blue in the face, but you know—against God and the Surgeon General . . . All right, no rebellion. We'll have to do it. And the boys needn't know about the big hubbub, it's not their fault. At any rate—all hands on deck tomorrow. Good night, gentlemen. By the way—as you know: England expects every man to do his duty."

This sentence wasn't tacked on the bulletin board. But, even in invisible form, Nelson's order of the day was out of place there: In the fourth year of the war nobody (that is, nobody except the big liar in Berlin) could afford ceremonious words —unless, of course, with quotation marks for irony. Whenever we didn't just keep silent, everybody preferred to stick to a motto like the simple "Duty is duty, and schnapps is schnapps."

But when things began to get serious on the next morning (right after ten-thirty the first Junkers 52 was announced just before it landed), things began to run very smoothly, procedures practiced hundreds of times—not like the empty ceremonial of a state visit, but, rather, like the precision-made timepiece of watchful love, something which had little to do with Hitler's war, but very much to do with mankind.

Like a whirlwind the ambulance drivers rushed out to the airport and then back with their human cargo—still as fast as possible—every minute is precious—but especially careful not to have to stop suddenly and to avoid any bump. They had learned that it has to be like music when you drive. "Do you know what an etude is? A kind of music with all notes the same. That's how you have to drive when you have wounded men—piano, pianissimo."

The corpsmen all had assigned places out front. Unload, don't bump—the sick charts for the NCO when he makes the assignments—careful, no mix-ups. Then—keep in step with the stretcher—if possible no talking until the patient is in bed. First aid can mean two things: a little joking and a look of calm, peppermint or lemon drops, a second wool blanket and a clean handkerchief.

And then the nurses—they've kept the tea hot and cooled down the fruit juice; a few heating pads—entirely too few— are on hand, the syringes have been sterilized, and the bandages are ready. And then one chore follows another. In normal times the jobs are separated a bit. Carrying heavy things should be a man's job, and then there are also unwritten laws of decorum. But then on a stormy day everybody who comes along does anything that has to be done. These men lying before them are children again, children who can't take care of themselves. True, they still don't stop being men, thirsty not for cherry juice and mineral water . . . but love comes in many guises. One is to light a cigarette for the man who doesn't have a hand free, to draw on it, and then stick it between the lips of the sick man, repeating this after each puff. Another, maybe, is to interpret rightly a slight sign of restlessness and then put the bottle on the right spot. . . .

It's no song of heroism. Nothing to sing about at all. But it is an answer to the question in the First Book. Question: Am I my brother's keeper? Answer: Yes.

It was a bad shipment. "Wretched, rotten," the first driver from the airport had called it. This time almost all were badly wounded; three who had died en route were brought to us first. This fact in itself was quite unusual; things must have looked bad where they came from. The living ones had precedence, but Klaus and I had to establish the identities of the dead right away and phone the burial officer in the city—in this severe cold it was nearly certain that there were no more graves prepared.

At meals you found only seven or eight people, and even then everybody sat in front of his plate as if on call. The chief medical officer and the surgeon's assistants stayed out of sight.

Right after eating I went first to the surgery ward; it was important to let one or two of those who couldn't write dictate a letter, just some sign of life. December 20th: Every letter sent off today might still reach a Christmas table somewhere in the dark Germany of 1943. A bit of hope—deceptive hope perhaps —but even at that not completely in vain. Something like certainty for the moment when uncertainty brought even more torment.

I entered the large hall and wrote letter after letter until Corpsman Wels called me to the dying man in the internal medicine wing.

[10]

NOW FOR THE REPORT ABOUT THE EVENTS AT WHICH I WAS NOT present. But when I add it all up—the Chief's description,

Nurse Ulrike's and Sergeant Major Hirzel's explanatory details, the orderly-room private's inserted comments, and, a long time after that December day, still another talk one evening with Dr. Wieland that touched on this dark half hour—when I add it all together, wasn't I there after all?

They came around four in the afternoon. The truck stopped about a hundred feet away from the front entrance, three young men in uniform jumped down from the back, the two goons jumped out of the front cab—the gentlemen from the SS; one a tub of lard and the other, almost more terrifying and repulsive, thin, alert, and observant with his little rat eyes wide open, filing away everything without a word. They came toward the clinic in a group of five; the young ones scurried on ahead and yanked both of the glass doors open so the two satraps could enter—or, as one ought to say, make their entrance. Their fecal-colored overcoats were open; they were lined in white lamb's skin from top to bottom.

"Where's the sergeant major around here?" the skinny one asked the enlisted corpsman, who had his desk near the entrance. But at the same moment the sergeant major himself came out of the orderly room, and, without any particular military bearing, gave his name.

The visitors didn't introduce themselves; the fat one—he was apparently in command—just pulled a piece of paper out of his cuff and clamped it between his teeth until his fur glove was buttoned again, and, still standing at the door to the orderly room, he said: "We're looking for the Jew"—then there came a name—"who works here as a stoker."

Hirzel, who had never heard Stefan's real name—the Chief had seen to it that "Stefan" was in all of the lists, and nothing else—Hirzel didn't grasp the situation in the first moment, but he did in the second and immediately was in full command of himself.

"There must be some mistake," he said. "There's nobody by that name known here."

"There is no mistake. We already know who we're looking for. Unknown—nonsense. The name is of no consequence; a real Hebrew has all kinds of names. One time it's Lewisohn, another time it's Sewerrot, or Solomon, or Siegfried. Got as many names as lice—have you got typhus here? Sure you've got typhus—"

He threw his head back, sniffed as if he might smell something, and began to hold forth: "Wherever the Jew is there are lice; where there are lice there's typhus—that's proven scientifically . . . you ought to know that in a clinic. All right then, where is the son of Abraham? I've got time. But of course not an unlimited amount. Ten minutes flat."

"I'll notify the chief medical officer right away."

"Completely unnecessary. Your chief has other things to do. Boy, you're on the ball! Probably never heard of the Jewish question, eh? When the exterminator comes to rid you of your vermin, you don't go inform the Chief. You're quite on your own authority here. Well, I'm a kind of Chief Exterminator— eh, Roedert?"

He turned to the man accompanying him who had been waiting in the outer office. "Move—swarm out. Get the man here!"

Whereupon Hirzel: "I have to get the Chief."

"Do whatever you have to—but *tempo presto,* if I may ask."

Five minutes went by. The visitors were alone with the orderly private.

"How long has the clinic been here?"

"A year and a half."

"You're living high on the hog here, it seems to me."

. . . .

"A pretty weary outfit?"

"No."

"But dyed-in-the-wool pious. I suppose you're a good Catholic?"

"No, a liberal non-denominational."

"Non-denominational, eh? 'Non-denom' is in your service record?"

"Yeah."

"You don't say. Well, one robin doesn't make it spring."

Then after a pause: "Where do you have a picture of the Führer around here?"

"We've already started packing up."

"A good excuse is worth a pile of money, but such a lame one—"

He didn't reach the end of the sentence. Chief Medical Officer Wieland entered; the sergeant major, who had come with him, went to his desk, got a key and gave the clerk a signal to leave the room with him.

"I'm Wieland."

"Kuortis."

"Roedert."

"We have an assignment here. To be carried out without delay for the security of the troops. A relocation action. Concerns the people of Israel. No objections can be considered."

Then, after a pause: "It's rather cold today. Tell me, could you scare up a cognac?"

Dr. Wieland assessed the situation quickly: snotty burglars with delusions of grandeur. He didn't offer them a chair but went to the door and called to the clerk waiting in the outer room: "Bring some cognac."

"Yessir, doctor. I'll bring the cognac."

Kuortis took his orders in his hands again—the execution order. "It has to do with a stoker here with you—"

"It has to do with a man who is absolutely indispensable in this building. Irreplaceable. We have five hundred wounded men here. If the heat doesn't work in our buildings—"

The cognac arrived. The corporal had brought along three glasses. "Pour for the gentlemen."

Kuortis: "Aren't you drinking?"

"I am on duty. We had a hundred and three new admissions today—seriously and very critically wounded men."

"I am very sorry. *We* didn't want to disturb you. But your sergeant—"

"The sergeant major conducted himself exactly according to regulations."

While they drank the cognac, no one offered a toast to them

(Wieland couldn't bring a "To your health" past his lips) and set the glasses down. With a carefully calculated gesture, one that was intended to appear like a blunder, the Chief swept both glasses from the table.

"Careful. Army property," said Kuortis. "I understand. You people don't want to drink from glasses touched by such sinful lips. Let's lay the cards on the table even if, as it appears, we don't love each other much. Doctor, sir, I find it understandable that you employed the man. Beggars can't be choosers. And the military accepts the services of a Jew. But it's over now. It may well be that the man *was* indispensable to you. But if the Russians get close next week—I say *if*—then all of these people that we haven't relocated two feet under will be partisans, and furthermore, partisans with specialized information. We cannot take this risk."

At that moment there was a knock on the door and the escort detail walked in. They brought Stefan—and Nurse Ulrike. Stefan had on a Red Cross nurse's cloak, obviously Nurse Ulrike's cloak. Poor feathered fellow—what nest did you fall from? Nurse Ulrike stood motionless next to Stefan.

Kuortis had his men step back; then, apparently determined to finish the scene, he pulled out his pistol.

"So that's our Israelite in whom there is no guile. Or is there guile? Hands up! Jew? No answer? Well, then, we'll have to ask the young lady for information. Funny, this little masquerade. A nurse's cloak for a disguise. That's quite original. Roedert, what do you say? Live and learn. 'Jew?' I asked. Not deaf but, regrettably, dumb. Well, the young lady certainly has, shall we say, physical evidence that he's not one of the *goyim*."

"Sir—" Wieland took a step toward the speaker. "I forbid you to insult my nurses. This nurse is the widow of an officer killed in action."

"The WCW? I know the type. The well-consoled widow." (At this remark—but this didn't come out until that later discussion—Nurse Ulrike's hand trembled. Up to that point she had been calmness personified—not a stony, stiff calmness, but perhaps more like the calmness of the "day that is without evening." The Chief thought: if she would just slap that guy right in the face. And thought: if she only doesn't lose her composure. Nurse Ulrike didn't lose it.)

"Listen to me for three more minutes, doctor. *Entre nous,* up till now I have diagnosed your humanitarian humbug as— I'm a man of feeling—well, as a children's disease. The falsification of identity which obviously was carried out here is of no interest to me; besides, all of us falsify something. But make no mistake: Whoever seriously opposes our principle of selection, we'll whack him down like a fly, you see—just like that. And as for your wound-cleaning and surgical-patchwork department —I can give you that in writing, I'm a man of feeling—well, with this ragtag and bobtail that crawls around here, the Führer can't build the new Europe. Not with that. We'll take our syringes without batting an eyelash and—"

Dr. Wieland interrupted his speech. "Your service record, please—" With two steps he reached the door.

"Sergeant Major Hirzel!"

Hirzel came.

"Make a note of his personal data—"

Kuortis, taken aback for only a moment, began to laugh.

"My service record? Well, now. Oh yes, my service record. You're a card. All right, then. With the greatest pleasure. You want to complain? Did I understand you correctly—complain? The Reichsheini will answer. Personally. By return mail. Unauthorized action with insufficient authority. Irresponsible rubbish. Vigorous action will be taken. Signed: Himmler, Heinrich. Irresponsible rubbish. I'll tell you who's responsible among us: Mister Nemo—nobody. 'Nobody has gouged out my eye.' You know, I'm sure: Homer, *The Odyssey.* Polyphemus. Nobody. What you've learned, you've learned. Why, I studied Greek with the Salesian friars. That sticks." Then: "Where is my service record? Did you take down the details, sergeant? Give it back to me. That's it. *Bon.*"

And then at the door: *"Do-svidanya,* doctor. Merry Christmas, everybody. And a very special nice little 'Heil Hitler' to your sexy little Florence Nightingales. I'm very sorry, madam, to have to bother you further. Take the coat off, Jew! Very amusing. Saint Martin and his cloak. But the Martinizing is over. The jig is up. Off to the merry chase!"

He stepped outside and fired in the air. The guard detail on the truck snapped to and saluted. Staff Doctor Jarisch, who had witnessed the departure of the desperados from a distance, followed them through the outer door. Then outside. When and through whom had little Leib heard about that afternoon's raid? Who had told him to bring his father his coat and the spoon for a journey for which neither coat nor spoon is needed? At any rate, his mother could not have told him. She didn't come until that moment when the boy had already climbed up on the truck and had been recognized by his father crouching up there. The boychik. The apple of his eye. The little one—and the whole of it—in what book is this? In the book of questions without answers.

[11]

ONLY THREE MORE POSTSCRIPTS. FIRST AN EXCERPT FROM THE sergeant major's report.

"When I noticed what was about to befall us, I had for the moment only two concerns: How can I get to my pistol—you never know about these things—and how can I work it so that the Chief will get here right away? The pistol was locked in my desk; the men were standing three steps away from me. It was impossible to get to the drawer. And the other thing was just as impossible; on such a hectic afternoon nobody could get the Chief to the telephone. Well, I went to the nearest phone, asked for the Chief in the most urgent manner possible—and, believe it or not, his 'Wieland' sounded—furious, of course, but now that was of no consequence. He must come over here right away, I said. 'Right away? What does "right away" mean? Just now a thigh case has arrived, and because of your call I'll have to start all over with my scrubbing. . . .' I said: 'It's the raid squad.' He: 'Listen, fellow, don't try anything funny.' I: 'I cannot explain it to you, sir, but—it has to be.' 'On your responsibility, sergeant?' he said then . . . He said it in such a voice that it made me freeze. What else could I answer but 'On my responsibility!'? On the way back I went by Sergeant Sander's, ripped open his locker, took his pistol and loaded it—just in case."

Nurse Ulrike told me: "It was a matter of two minutes. First I had a head start. You had told me yesterday where Stefan could most likely be found. I was sitting at the mail desk when they came in and was able to get away with a couple of packages without attracting attention. I got down there right away. Naturally I couldn't yell out loud, but in my loudest whisper —there *is* such a thing—I kept saying: Stefan, Stefan. Then I found him and explained to him quickly what had happened. But then I had to practically force him away from the place. As for the coat—oh, one just does something or other. If only these lights hadn't been burning all over the place. . . . Two of the men came from one side. Maybe we could still have gotten out, but I don't know my way around there, and Stefan, you know, Stefan didn't want to move. At the last moment I thought: Maybe a brazen reply will work. Both of them came and asked: 'What are you doing here?' And I, as nasty as possible: 'Well, you can see, can't you? We're looking for a defective spot. If in this wretched cold—' But I didn't get any farther. For now they were saying to Stefan: 'And you?' I had just put the cape over him at the last second . . . but then it was already over. They called the third man who had been looking at another place and took us both up between them."

Much later there was another conversation with the chief medical officer.

"Remember the leader of the gang that grabbed Stefan from

us that time? I told you about that—how he burst out laughing when I demanded his service record from him. What kind of laughter was that?"

I asked in return: "You did report the incident at that time, Dr. Wieland?"

"Of course. But my complaint just came back with a note saying that it was not in the jurisdiction of the recipient."

"Then it was almost exactly what the man had predicted with his speech about Polyphemus. He knew his men—or, rather, his superior bandits. What do you call that, a retreat forward or something? Tell the truth; it will be the most unlikely thing possible. But what about the other thing, that threat that they were going to murder the war victims; what do you think?"

"That was his own idea. Or are there such plans? I wouldn't put anything past them, nothing whatever."

"Extermination—I read that word once. A rather graphic word, I must say. This is their master plan."

"Hm. But the mass murderers themselves want to survive. Of course, this Kuortis—wasn't that his name?—he was a *va banque* gambler, the epitome of an 'all-or-nothing man.' 'Himmler, Heinrich' and this 'nice little Heil Hitler,' do you remember? That's all he had left. Only this repulsive attack on Nurse Ulrike. Is this the way the world is laid out? Shabby reduction to . . . ah, well . . ."

"And power? Power *per se*. Power: the lust of the impotent. Or should one say: executions for variety in erotic monotony? Is that what it all adds up to? I don't know, doctor, I don't know."

"Dear God above—excuse me, pastor—is that what man is?"

"Yes, I believe so—that too, Dr. Wieland. That is what he is also."

At the time of this conversation the Hungarian summer was all around us—the vast sky above the plains, quaking-grass and the flight of doves. For a moment here and there the world looked like peace again. But the Red Army was not very far even from there. And the wolves among our own, now without sheep's clothing, had followed us here hard on our heels. They were plying their trade again. They could be standing there tomorrow. Kuortis, Roedert.

[12]

BUT ON THAT TWENTIETH OF DECEMBER—TO TELL ABOUT THIS last—supper was at seven o'clock in the officers' club as always; and even though there was still work to be done right into the night, now we were at least all together. It turned out to be a silent meal. Stefan—what law might it be that ruled here?— wasn't a topic of conversation for us even today; and as for those discussions with which the world kills time—"Talks about . . . ," "Concerning *the* Jews," for example,—they would have led, even at our round table for certain, to no other goal than that which they always reach: Babel. But in those days we were on guard against such discussions. We did the best we could—or, if not the best, then what was not altogether inappropriate: We kept silent. The curtains here in the hall had already been taken down in preparation for our departure, which was now undoubtedly imminent. The nocturnal sky appeared through the large windows. Starkly dark winter blue, later bright blue, then finally violet—those had been the colors of the afternoon. Now there were yellow streaks which the still invisible moon was painting across the blackness of the horizon. Not a single star.

"Red wine, please," said the Chief to the orderly as the vegetables were passed to him a second time, and at the same time his glance fell upon Head Paymaster Federlein, who was in charge of a supply of wine reserved for emergencies and holiday festivities. Federlein understood the request immediately and gave the orderly a key. Glasses were brought in, medium-sized, dull-colored glasses. When all had been served, the Chief stood up; it looked as if he wanted to say something. And as though upon a secret command, we too arose. Dr. Wieland moved his lips, but not a word came out. Thus we drank in silence: a stark, worldly sacrament that allowed of no moving of the lips, no craning of the neck and hardly a glance around. Whom were we toasting? Then we sat down again, and even now no one wanted to disturb the somber funeral feast with any kind of words.

Why did I say to Nurse Ulrike, "Stefan is the stoker?" Did I in this way become a sharer in the guilt of her rescue attempt that thwarted every possibility of rescue? And: What was I to do now with the candle, the candle promised to the boychik, the candle for the Feast of Hanukah? "Seventeen," the one in the drab lambskin coat had called out before he got back into the driver's cab. But no number counts here. Let it be a thousand times a thousand, or let it be one, just one, only Leib; any one alone means destruction. The bark is ripped open, the good bark on the tree of life.

What does this mean: It cramps your heartstrings? I've known it since that evening hour. For it was just such a cramp that crushed the glass I was holding tightly. The splinters cut into three fingers of my right hand, and, as is always the case with me, it began to bleed profusely. Pharmacist Jablonski, who was sitting across from me, noticed it almost at the same moment I noticed it. "Chaplain, sir, what on earth are you doing? Are you a glass eater? . . . Wait a moment, I just happen to have some bandages over there." He had deposited some bandaging material on a side table. He brought the right things; Dr. Braun, next to me at the table, bandaged me up. And in this way, in the little tempest of life, the strange meal ended.

In the midst of this unrest, the Chief had given the signal for us to stand; now he came over to us and, after a glance at my hand, said, "I have to go back to my ward once more; when you're finished here, Braun, come over too."

"We'll be finished right away," said Dr. Braun, whereupon I

said to the Chief: "I'm sorry to have caused the turmoil. It must have been a real cramp in my hand."

"No wonder," said Dr. Wieland and nodded to me.

"Well, *reverendissime*, I think that'll hold it. It'll be healed right before the end of the war. The saying doesn't always fit; but I think we can consider it applicable here."

"Thank you very much, Dr. Braun. And many thanks to you too, Mr. Jablonski. It was good that you happened to have the bandages."

"Come on now. Don't mention it. . . ."

Staff Doctor Jarisch had just watched as I was being given first-aid. I was about to hold out my hand—the left one—as a good-night gesture when he urged me over to the window with an almost timid motion. He looked out into the vague darkness for a good while, and it was not difficult to determine where he was glancing. Then he started to leave.

"Did you see how the little boy jumped up into the truck a while ago? And what a pretty little spoon he had stuck in his side? It was just like a dress sword—the kind a knight used to carry."

"Yes," I said. "Yes, Dr. Jarisch, I saw it."

PERSONAL ENCOUNTERS WITH
MARTIN BUBER

Albrecht Goes ✡ MARTIN BUBER, A LIVING LEGEND

An Address Delivered at the University of Frankfurt
On Martin Buber's 80th Birthday, February 8, 1958

[1]

A LIVING LEGEND. . . . LET ME TELL YOU FIRST HOW I ARRIVED at this title for my talk, and then you need not fear that you will be regaled with anecdotes any further.

One afternoon, following a formal address given by Martin Buber that morning, a small group of us were gathered, with the venerable man in our midst. We were tired and relaxed. The presence of a sick woman who was looking over to us from her sofa gave our gathering a peculiar aura of reality—I am almost tempted to say, intimacy. You know how under such circumstances one sometimes speaks a word that would not pass one's lips in a more formal situation—and so I said then: "When Martin Buber is in our midst, then, I think, one's primary feeling is not one of being in the presence of a scholar, a philosopher, a man of original thought, but, rather, the idea that God's story continues, the story of Abraham and Isaiah; the eternal voice is not silent." How easily such a bold statement could have caused confusion! But Martin Buber looked at me with wonderful composure and asked cheerfully: "Then that would be a kind of existence as a legend?" To which I replied: "Yes, if you accept the assumption that a legend is something eminently real." Whereupon he said: "Then I shall have to tell you what happened to me when I met Edmund Husserl thirty years ago. A lecture by Husserl had been announced, and I was anxious to hear him. When I entered the hall, someone from the Philosophical Society recognized me, and right away I was asked to sit at a kind of head table. When Husserl appeared, he gave us a quick greeting before stepping up to the lectern. 'My name is Buber,' I said. He was taken aback for a moment and asked: 'The real Buber?' I hesitated to give any further explanation, whereupon Husserl said: But there is no such person! Buber—why, that's a legend!' "

What an incident! A fifty-year-old man appears to his contemporaries and colleagues as a "legendary figure." "But there is no such person!" This sounds like open astonishment at the fact that a bit of magic turns into reality, that a secret reveals itself.

Here we are not concerned with the pseudo-halo of legends artificially created, with the dubious aura about ivory towers. The man whose eightieth birthday was celebrated yesterday in Jerusalem and all over the world has never lived in the market place and even less in an ivory tower. It would take someone acquainted with all relationships, one with an inside knowledge—I mean a Jewish expert—to tell us what Martin Buber's existence has meant to the Jewish people the world over during the past half-century. He would show us how they are all one: the young student in Vienna gripped by Herzl's Zionist call; the professor at Heppenheim and Frankfurt-am-Main who knew how to remind a much-scattered people of its unity, of the first, the oldest, the ever-lasting covenant; and that old man in Jerusalem who may occasionally be seen on photos, standing in a lecture room and surrounded by sparkling young Israelis. "To be old"—we are reminded of Buber's remark about Natorp—"to be old is a glorious thing when one has not unlearned what it means *to begin*. . . ." And further (Natorp or Buber, as you prefer): "He was not at all young, but he was

old in a young way, knowing how to begin." [1] And one also
fleetingly remembered that the Baal-Shem-Tov himself, the
founder of Hasidism, had once been a teacher of children.

A Legend. . . . This word rings up three associations. First:
We neither know nor care to know the complete *curriculum
vitae,* the stark biographical facts; it is enough if a few moments of fulfillment stand out for us. Then: Life as a legend is
to be understood as life under the open sky, "in the countenance of God"—in Buber's language: "Legend is the myth of
the I and Thou, of the called one and the calling one." [2] And
finally (and this is what was meant by my daring statement of
that afternoon): Such a life is essentially one that is not self-
sufficient and does not interpret itself, but points away from
itself. This pointing of the way to be sure, this task of tran-
scending the self, can only be accomplished with composure of
the soul, by the whole person. And both this spiritual concentration and this pointing of the way beyond the self are contained in words which Buber discovered as his command, and
his command is always first a command to himself: "You shall
not withhold yourself." [3]

[2]

WHEN HAD THAT BEGUN? "WHEN I WAS A CHILD"—SIGNIFICANTLY
enough, this man, so sparing in his personal references, places
this memoir at the conclusion of his first address on Judaism—
"I read an old Jewish tale I could not understand. It said no

[1] *Eclipse of God:* Studies in the Relation Between Religion and Philosophy (New York: Harper Torchbooks, 1957), "Prelude: Report on Two
Talks," translated by Maurice S. Friedman, p. 6; Paul Natorp (1854–1924):
educator and Professor of Philosophy in Marburg, who, along with Hermann Cohen, headed the neo-Kantian "Marburg school."

[2] *The Legend of the Baal-Shem* (New York: Harper & Bros., 1956), p. xiii.

[3] *Pointing the Way,* translated, edited, and with a new introduction by
Maurice S. Friedman (New York: Harper Torchbooks, 1963), pp. 109–110.

188   MEN OF DIALOGUE

more than this: 'Outside the gates of Rome there sits a leprous beggar, waiting. He is the Messiah.' Then I came upon an old man whom I asked: 'What is he waiting for?' And the old man gave me an answer I did not understand at the time, an answer I learned to understand only much later. He said: 'He waits for you.' " [4]

"He waits for you." Of course—that could not be understood then. But there were some glowing signs which pointed in that direction.

There was the childhood in Lvov, in the house of his grandfather, Salomon Buber, the Midrash scholar, for whom the Talmud was "an organic possession of the whole person." There were the walks out into the small country town of Sadagora, in which a Hasidic tradition was still alive. True, the shining strength of the first and second generation of Hasidism was gone; but the boy did see "genuine community and genuine leadership" as the living dual core of humanity. "Ancient past, farthest future were here, lost, longed for, returned." [5] And here we must name specifically that experience which is remembered in the book Dialogue, where the author comes to speak of the destructive power of a "reflection," a bending back to one's self, something that breaks through the blessed cycle of call and responsibility. It is a boyhood experience with a horse which was familiar and then suddenly turned so unfamiliar. "When I was eleven years of age, spending the summer on my grandparents' estate, I used, as often as I could do it unobserved, to steal into the stable and gently stroke the neck of my darling, a broad dapple-gray horse. . . . I must say that what I experienced in touch with the animal was the Other, the immense otherness of the Other, which, however, did not remain strange . . . but rather let me draw near and touch it. . . . The horse . . . very gently raised his massive head,

4 On Judaism, edited by Nahum N. Glatzer (New York: Schocken Books, 1967), "Judaism and the Jews," translated by Eva Jospe, p. 21.

5 Hasidism and Modern Man, edited and translated by Maurice Friedman (New York: Harper Torchbooks, 1966), p. 53.

ears flicking, then snorted quietly . . . ; and I was approved. But once . . . it struck me about the stroking, what fun it gave me, and suddenly I became conscious of my hand. The same went on as before, but something had changed, it was no longer the same thing. And the next day . . . when I stroked my friend's head he did not raise his head. A few years later, when I thought back to the incident, I no longer supposed that the animal had noticed my defection. But at the same time I considered myself judged." [6]

These three experiences, then, had sunk in: The recognition of the majesty of that which is enduring, the everlasting "Shema Israel"; the presentiment of a possibility of renewal out of the elemental; and also another presentiment: that danger lurks on the way from me to the other one, that it is we ourselves who endanger the unconstrained nature of an I–Thou relationship.

But then the circle widened, and into the view of the young man eager for life and learning came the Vienna of the turn of the century, that exceedingly rich, colorful and fragrant sphere which in Stefan Zweig's *The World of Yesterday* is conjured up from living memory "in farewell's blazing gloss" [7] and which, solving all problems by giving them form, will shine forever in the early works of Hofmannsthal.

Whatever the Viennese student took up—literature, art, history, philosophy—with the span ranging from Dilthey to Nietzsche and including in particular the mysticism of Meister Eckhart and Angelus Silesius; and whatever came his way—the world of the theater above all, three flights up in the Burgtheater on the highest balcony; the magic of Chinese ghosts and games; the Kalewala, the Finnish national epic: All these

---

[6] *Between Man and Man,* with an Introduction by Maurice Friedman and an Afterword by the author on "The History of the Dialogical Principle," translated by Ronald Gregor Smith and Maurice Friedman (New York: Macmillan Paperbacks, 1965), p. 23.

[7] "Im Glast des Scheidelichts"—a phrase from Stefan Zweig's last poem, "Der Sechzigjährige dankt."—Eds.

things remained his permanent possession. To be sure, there is a way of looking at things—and Buber is familiar with it—which interprets this multicolored diversity as a "world of confusion" and which will not give its approval until the two great areas of responsibility of those years have taken hold in the life of the adept—the Zionist idea and the Socialist heritage, Buber having taken up the latter with an early passion. To my mind, however, another intrinsically important feature in Martin Buber's life and work is the fact that the beautiful in a multitude of forms, including "ailing Austria," was able to seek its due. Whoever looks at men's careers notices again and again that two questions are of importance: how much nature, breadth, health, originality a man possesses and how bold the span is, how far apart the stakes are placed in the zestful growth of his years as an apprentice and journeyman. In "To the Contemporary," a rhapsodic essay which Buber wrote in the Fall of 1914, a stirring moment in world history, it comes to light that this life can never fear its own excess, its overabundance, its extravagance; the only things it could be afraid of might be curtailment, atrophy, negation. "Never again, O moment, O instorming power of the contemporary," he says in this essay, "never will I bid you go. You shall stay with me and no one will efface you. Rather shall I be prey and fuel to your fire all the moments of my life. Out of your fire light is born, and nowhere does it flash except out of your fire. I am consumed in you, but I am consumed into light." [8]

[3]

THERE, IN THE MIDST OF HIS HUMANISTIC EXCURSION, BUBER EN-counters the *zevaat ribesh,* the legacy of the Baal-Shem-Tov. And the man—no longer the boy of Sadagora—read: "He arises from sleep with fervor, for he is hallowed and become

[8] *Pointing the Way,* p. 60.

another man and is worthy to create and is become like the Holy One, blessed be He, when He created His world." "It was then"—so Buber describes his hour—"that, overpowered in an instant, I experienced the Hasidic soul." [9] There was the message, the old one from Isaiah, "The whole earth is full of His glory," and the words from the Kabbala, "No place without Him"; and there were the leaders of those pious men, the *zaddikim:* first and foremost the Baal-Shem, the great Maggid, the Seer of Lublin, the Rižiner—all of those who passed on the golden bucket as a living chain, who passed on the insight that "God can be beheld in each thing and reached through each pure deed." [10]

Five years of Buber's life were now devoted to the assignment of becoming aware of this reality, and fifty more years to the task of transmitting the vital sources which were here released, of freeing tradition from the entanglements and excrescences of later additions, of presenting ever more simply, more clearly, and more succinctly what belongs together: the moment of life and the word of truth from this moment. And in so doing one thing was always testified to: that the glory of God has been given to the world in all its multiplicity, order, and disorder, but that there is a possibility of rediscovering in all places—in the ritual bath and at the inn, when baking bread, in conversation, in the street—the traces of man's having been created in God's image, of discovering the sparks of this glory even in the abyss and viewing evil itself as the bramble which *wills* to be seized by the divine fire.

To a man who is vouchsafed such an encounter, it is—like a love encounter—something immeasurable; it befalls one, it happens. And he to whom it happens does not know what befalls him.

In the task which Buber saw before him—the regeneration of Judaism, a renewed awareness of its unity and its future, his encounter with Hasidism meant the help of a new dimension.

[9] *Hasidism and Modern Man*, p. 59.
[10] *Ibid.*, p. 49.

And yet this experience, too, could remain only a step. In the foreword to his book *For the Sake of Heaven,* in which Martin Buber tells the Hasidic story of "Power and Grace," he already points the way toward new territory: "I, myself, have no 'doctrine.' . . . He who expects of me a teaching . . . will always be disillusioned. And it would seem to me, indeed, that in this hour of history the crucial thing is not to possess a fixed doctrine, but rather to recognize eternal reality and out of its depth to be able to face the reality of the present. No way can be pointed to in this desert night. One's purpose must be to help men of today to stand fast, with their souls in readiness, until the dawn breaks and a path becomes visible where none suspected it." [11] In the Hasidic experience (an experience for which the word "mysticism" is but an inadequte designation) he had just found that concepts like people, language, image, beauty, humanism are not binding on a person unless there is also a bond with the eternal—that is to say, if there is no religion. (And here is the point where the parallel to Schleiermacher becomes inescapable: A hundred years before Buber, in a somewhat related hour, there was the same strength to absorb what was at hand and to be concerned with the eternal in the midst of it.) At that point Buber himself ventures an objection: "Nowadays 'religion' itself is part of the detached spirit. It is one of the subdivisions—one which is in high favor, to be sure—of the structures erected over and above life . . . but this sort of religion is not an entity which includes all of life. . . ." [12] And then, stated positively in *Dialogue:* "Above and below are bound to one another. The word of him who wishes to speak with men without speaking with God is not fulfilled; but the word of him who wishes to speak with God without speaking with men goes astray. There is a tale that a

11 *For the Sake of Heaven: A Chronicle,* translated by Ludwig Lewisohn (Cleveland and New York: The World Publishing Company; Philadelphia: The Jewish Publication Society of America, 1958, 1961), p. xiii.

12 *Israel and the World: Essays in a Time of Crisis* (New York: Schocken Books, second edition, 1963), pp. 90–91.

man inspired by God once went out from the creaturely realms into the vast waste. There he wandered till he came to the gates of the mystery. He knocked. From within came the cry: 'What do you want here?' He said, 'I have proclaimed your praise in the ears of mortals, but they were deaf to me. So I come to you that you yourself may hear me and reply.' 'Turn back,' came the cry from within. 'Here is no ear for you. I have sunk my hearing in the deafness of mortals.' True address from God directs man into the place of lived speech, where the voices of the creatures grope past one another, and in their very missing of one another succeed in reaching the eternal partner." [13]

Buber's task now looks like this: to listen for the "deafness of mortals" in the "realm of lived speech"—divine service, understood as human service, as solicitude about experiencing in the midst of dreariness, inhibitions, routine toil, a breakthrough—not a breakthrough of mystical rapture but one of human encounter; about experiencing the grace and happiness of "dialogic life." "The life of dialogue"—according to one of the numerous formulations Buber found here—is not one in which you have much to do with men, but one in which you really have to do with those with whom you have to do." [14]

[4]

PART OF BUBER'S IMAGE IS HEALTH—PHYSICAL AS WELL AS MENtal health, the fresh, wide-open eyes which delight in looking at nature, created things, human beings, structures, works of art. To Buber belongs also the organic growth of his intellectual world; as each new step is reached, the previous one does not become outmoded, is not negated, but is subsumed and cherished. Two prizes conferred upon him in Germany were

13 *Between Man and Man*, p. 15.
14 *Ibid.*, p. 20.

the Peace Prize of the German Book Trade and the prize that
bears Goethe's name; people spontaneously sensed the appro-
priateness of both, even the second one. With a "fresh, healthy
glance," to use a Goethean phrase, Buber had taken in the
fullness of the world and of life, had perceived the phenomenon of Hasidism, worked out within himself experiences of
his own existential philosophy, had received and imparted
knowledge. Now he was impelled with renewed urgency to
proceed on the road to knowledge—to his comprehensive
translation of the Holy Scripture of the Old Testament.

The question concerning the nature of prophecy; the significance of the Messianic idea; the points of juncture between the
Old and the New Testaments; the mystery of Biblical leadership—all these things presented themselves to him, and all the
insights he had gathered up to then were put in the service of
this work. The important thing was to become aware—with
exactness and openness, with sober confidence ("sober" and
"confidence" are Buberian words)—of where these words of
Scripture come from and where they are going.

To begin with the second point: Buber seeks to view man
anew and concretely in his capacity as recipient of the message,
to see the Bible reader of the present, and he describes him and
his situation thus: "He must face the book with a new attitude
as something new. . . . He does not know which of its sayings
and images will overwhelm him and mold him, from where the
spirit will ferment and enter into him, to incorporate itself
anew in his body. But he holds himself open. He does not believe anything a priori; he does not disbelieve anything a
priori." [15]

And then: What about the word itself? Where does it come
from? The realms of orthodoxy had become inaccessible, the
results of Old Testament scholarship of the nineteenth century
in particular had become inescapable. In Buber's bold formu-
lation it reads thus: "Do we mean a book? We mean the

[15] *Israel and the World*, p. 93.

voice!" [16] And here a gate was opened—not for dreamy caprice, but for that obedient freedom which harkens beyond the letter toward the life-giving spirit.

It is not possible in this context to do justice to Martin Buber's new translation of the Scripture (which he began in collaboration with Franz Rosenzweig), or to retrace the steps back to the roots and out to the venture of a sacral language. But, if you will permit me an analogy, it would be like talking about Mozart on a Mozart anniversary without playing Mozart if we were to celebrate this festive day without making audible for a moment how the Scripture sounds as put into German by Martin Buber. Balaam's speech from Numbers 24 goes like this:

> *Bilam erhob seine Augen*
> *und sah Jisrael wohnend nach seinen Zweigen*
> *und über ihm war der Geistbraus Gottes.*
> *Er hub sein Gleichwort an, er sprach:*
> *Erlauten Bilams des Borsohns,*
>
> *Erlauten des Mannes erschlossnen Augs.*
> *Erlauten des Hörers göttlicher Sprüche,*
> *der die Schau des Gewaltigen schaut,*
> *hinsinkend, bar die Augen:*
> *wie sind deine Zelte, Jaakob, schön,*
> *deine Wohnungen, Jisrael!*
> *Wie Bachgründe, gebogen,*
> *wie Gärten am Strom,*
> *wie Aloen, die Er pflanzte,*
> *wie Zedern am Wasser!*
> *Wasser rinnt von seinen Trieben,*
> *in vielem Wasser ist seine Saat.*

[16] A postscript added by Buber to the reference in note 15 above and apparently not published in English translation. The original German quotation is in *Schriften zur Bibel*, Vol. II of Martin Buber's *Werke* (Munich: Kösel-Verlag; Heidelberg: Lambert Schneider, 1964), p. 869.

"As Balaam looked up and saw Israel encamped tribe by tribe, the spirit of God came upon him. Taking up his theme, he said:

> *Word of Balaam son of Beor,*
> *Word of the man whose eye is true,*
> *Word of him who hears God's speech,*
> *Who beholds visions from the Almighty,*
> *Prostrate but with eyes unveiled:*
> *How fair are your tents, O Jacob,*
> *Your dwellings, O Israel!*
> *Like palm-groves that stretch out,*
> *Like gardens beside a river,*
> *Like aloes planted by the* LORD,
> *Like cedars beside the water;*
> *Their boughs drip with moisture,*
> *Their roots have abundant water.*[17]

[5]

A LIVING LEGEND. . . . HE WHO APPROACHES MARTIN BUBER TO observe him would not want to belong to the "masses" about which he himself has said, severely but not unjustly that they do not know what to do with man, with the strenuous marvel of his multiplicity, and they demand instead a convenient index entry.

The strenuous—or more accurately, the gratifying—marvel of Martin Buber's multiplicity makes it difficult to give this living legend a name; such a name would have to be a very open and broad one. It is easier to characterize the life element of this man. It is neither earth nor fire, nor is it the storm; it is the streaming current. The materials with which he works can also be more easily described. I shall name three of them, all akin to water: zeal, patience—and cheerfulness.

"Let him arise from sleep with fervor"—we read in that

[17] From *The Torah,* Jewish Publication Society translation, Philadelphia, 1962.

work of the Baal-Shem-Tov which has become something like a summons for Buber. But this is not the zeal of the zealot who destroys, nor the fanatical passion which destroys in its "zeal for the House of God." There is fighting, to be sure. In coming to terms with the modern existentialist philosophy Buber carefully examines whether where one says "God" an eclipse of God does not really hold sway—because no vis-à-vis is being addressed, no true answer is given to any "And God spoke." But Buber's zeal is devoid of feverishness, nor is he frightened by doubts. The reality of a world that is inimical to mystery calls forth in him nothing but serene confidence: The fictitious mysteries will disappear; the genuine mystery will arise.

Martin Buber is an educator by nature and by grace; he is possessed of the cardinal virtue of the educator—patience. It accompanied him along the road of Zionist aspirations; it was part of his work in adult education classes after the First World War, at the University of Frankfurt, and at the *Mittelstelle für jüdische Erwachsenenbildung* [Center for Jewish Adult Education] in the early years of the Hitler regime. His patience bade him hold out in the midst of the hostile flood here in Germany, as someone who has been more inclined toward *quantum satis* [as much as suffices] than toward "all or nothing." When he was to move into a new area, the professorship for Social Philosophy at the Hebrew University in Jerusalem, he found, at the conclusion of his inaugural lecture, the perfect formula for patience—not the patience of the researcher alone, but that of all human existence. The concluding sentences read: "There are situations in the lives of peoples in which the people becomes, as it were, plastic, and the impossible becomes possible. Perhaps such an hour is near. We think of this 'perhaps' when we perform our service. We would also perform it, of course, if this possibility did not exist. For, resigned or unresigned, the spirit works." [18]

The spirit works, the spirit is at work. . . . No one reflects on Buber without feeling the calm, intensively searching eyes

18 *Pointing the Way*, p. 191.

of the man directed at him. We are indebted to him for some pen portraits of friends: Moritz Heimann, Gustav Landauer, Franz Rosenzweig. Apart from that which distinguishes Buber's entire work—the pure light of his language, the severe, Hofmannsthal-like grace—what distinguishes these portraits? It is patience, and here it has allowed to come into being something intensive, careful, deliberated from many angles, yet nothing definitive, nothing irrevocable. Or one thinks of Buber's description of some variety of man, such as that of the "erotic man" from the book *Dialogue*. Two things are at work: an unerring clairvoyance, one that finds phenomena even in their hiding places; and the capacity to hesitate. This particular capacity is very important; an impatient man has finite reality at his disposal, but the hesitantly patient man is in league with the infinite possibilities of phenomena. But let us hear Buber himself: "Many years I have wandered through the land of men, and have not yet reached an end of studying the varieties of the 'erotic man.' . . . There a lover stamps around and is in love only with his passion. There one is wearing his differentiated feelings like medal-ribbons. There one is enjoying the adventures of his own fascinating effect. There one is gazing enraptured at the spectacle of his own supposed surrender. There one is collecting excitement. There one is displaying his 'power.' There one is preening himself with borrowed vitality. There one is delighting to exist simultaneously as himself and as an idol very unlike himself. There one is warming himself at the blaze of what has fallen to his lot. There one is experimenting. And so on and on—all the manifold monologists with their mirrors, in the apartment of the most intimate dialogue!" [19]

Finally, the cheerfulness. "Cleverness without heart is nothing at all. Piety is false." Buber approvingly cites this Hasidic saying in an argument with Karl Barth in which he addresses the author of *Church Dogmatics* on the joyous basis of Hasidic beliefs: "But I would, I could, show Karl Barth here, in Jeru-

[19] *Between Man and Man*, pp. 29–30.

salem, how the Hasidim dance the freedom of the heart to the fellow man." [20] One cannot speak of Martin Buber without speaking of his cheerfulness and its only stable basis, the love of humankind. We must remember Buber's highly significant decision in favor of man in all his dubiousness. "The world," so he once wrote, "has dark bread for me on whose crust I loosen my teeth and with which I am never sated: people. Oh, these muddle-heads and ne'er-do-wells, how I love them!" And in the same reflection, in which the question "books and people?" or "books or people?" is discussed, he goes on to say: "I knew nothing of books when I sprang from my mother's womb, and I want to die without books, with a human hand clasping mine. Now, to be sure, I sometimes close the door to my room and surrender to a book, but only because I can open the door again and see a human being looking up at me." [21]

[6]

WHAT NAME, THEN—IF WE ARE TO VENTURE A NAME—SHALL WE give to this "living legend"? What shall we call the mainspring that has operated this clock for eighty years now? (And what years!) I shall call it *the venture of reconciliation.*

A venture. . . . It is impossible to impute an illusory love to this man, impossible to think that he is blind to the evil, the obdurateness of yesterday and today, the impudence, the incorrigibility, the disunion. Anyone who here synthesizes in deed or thought must know that he is undertaking a venture.

Reconciliation. . . . Why is there reconciliation? Reconcil-

20 This quotation and the one preceding it are from Martin Buber, *Between Man and Man* (New York: Macmillan Paperback Edition, 1965), "Afterword: The History of the Dialogical Principle," translated by Maurice Friedman, p. 224.

21 Buber's "Books and People" is included in the present volume on pp. 28–29.

iation is based on the insight that we are sons, I and the other. There is reconciliation before the countenance of the Eternal Father. It is a piece of the creed—or it is not.

We think of everything disunited—of the venture of a reconciliation between generations, to avoid beginning with the hardest. We see Buber, the oldest, resembling the patriarch from Rymanov, effortlessly being close to the youngest because his faculty to be astonished has not flagged. Thus it was in Germany of yesterday and today, thus it is in Israel. Already the third generation is sitting at his feet. "What did he say?" we ask the young people when they tell us about their visits to Buber, and then they describe the man, the prophetic figure. We could pour cold water on their enthusiasm and tell them that Buber wants listeners to what he has to say, not admirers of his person or any person. But since the man's words are truthful, who would separate the person and the cause?

Reconciliation of classes. . . . There is a worker who asks questions, profoundly and urgently, and a professor who gives him answers. The listener closes the conversation by saying simply, "You are right." But the professor, having a more accurate estimate of the real distance and thinking of himself and his lot, has to continue: "I could not remain, as I now ought to do; I could not enter into the factory where the man worked, become his comrade, live with him, win his trust through real life-relationship, help him to walk with me the way of the creature who *accepts* the creation. I could only return his gaze." [22]

Reconciliation of nations. . . . We see Buber, a professor at the Hebrew University, living for many years in the house of an Arab—his own way of overcoming the grave conflict. We can still hear the words that were spoken in September, 1953, in St. Paul's Church at Frankfurt, spoken in the language of the people of which millions of Buber's co-religionists were

[22] Paul Arthur Schilpp and Maurice Friedman, editors, *The Philosophy of Martin Buber*, Vol. XII of *The Library of Living Philosophers* (La Salle, Illinois: Open Court, 1967), pp. 28–29; and *Eclipse of God*, p. 6.

murdered: "What am I that I could here presume to 'forgive'!" And: "But my heart, which is acquainted with the weakness of men, refuses to condemn my neighbor for not prevailing upon himself to become a martyr." [23]

Reconciliation. . . . We remember the Christian-Jewish religious dialogue which took place twenty-five years ago, just before the outbreak of the devilry, at the *Lehrhaus* in Stuttgart, and Buber's description of how he saw in the city of Worms both the dome in its harmony and the old Jewish cemetery. . . . "Nothing can divert me from the God-time of Israel." [24] In his study, *Martin Buber und das Christentum,* Urs von Balthasar recently posed the question which Buber has been asked time and time again: Did he, in his concern with the figure of Jesus against his own Jewish background and in his consideration of God's servant, perhaps include material borrowed from the New Testament in his Old Testament theology after all? Writing in a tone of profound reverence, Balthasar assures us pointedly that "the ringing hardness of what clashes here sounds more beautiful than a harmless drawingroom conversation about the contribution of Hasidism to world religion and the eminent practicality of the dialogical principle." [25] Here it is a matter of one view against another. But I believe that Buber, who means reconciliation but not conformity, will be satisfied if the sons are together—in the dialogue of silence, of hope and insufficiency, in the "sighing of living creatures."

[23] *A Believing Humanism: My Testament 1902–1965,* series Credo Perspectives, planned and edited by Ruth Nanda Anshen, translated and with an Introduction and Explanatory Comments by Maurice Friedman (New York: Simon and Schuster, 1967), pp. 195–196; and *Pointing the Way,* p. 233.

[24] In *Christianity: Some Non-Christian Appraisals,* edited by David W. McKain (New York: McGraw-Hill Book Company, 1964), Martin Buber, "Church, State, Nation, Jewry," translated by William Hallo, p. 187; also included in the present volume as "Second Response," pp. 220–224.

[25] Hans Urs von Balthasar, *Einsame Zwiesprache: Martin Buber und das Christentum* (Cologne and Olten: Verlag Jakob Hegner, 1958).

Zeal, patience, cheerfulness—and why have hope for this venture? It is the Hasidic faith, the belief in the sparks of glory embedded in the depths of the world which empowers Buber to think of both things at once—of God's time and patience, and of the immeasurable grace of the moment which is vouchsafed to those who seize the responsibility in the moment. This is the subject of that great description of a picture in which Buber answers the question about man's potential: ". . . the man who hourly measures the depths of responsibility with the sounding lead of his words. He speaks—and knows that his speech is destiny. He does not decide the fate of countries and peoples, but ever again only the small and great course of an individual life, so finite and yet so boundless. Men come to him, and each desires his opinion, his help. And even though it is corporal and semi-corporal needs that they bring to him, in his world-insight there is nothing corporal that cannot be transfigured, nothing material that cannot be raised to spirit. And it is this that he does for all: *he elevates their need before he satisfies it.* Thus he is the helper in spirit, the teacher of world-meaning, the conveyor to the divine sparks. The world needs him, the perfected man; it awaits him, it awaits him ever again." [26]

[7]

AT TIMES—AND I SAY THIS IN CONCLUSION—I HARBOR THE IDEA that man, in his best aspects, is a greeting—no more and no less. A greeting: this means "not yet," Moses *outside* the Promised Land; but it *is* a cue, a sign, a message nearly decoded. The number of greetings is not inconsiderable, and a particular one is firmly implanted in each of us. May we recognize it: "Hark!" and "Peace!" and "Be watchful!" and "Be of good cheer!" and "What is man?"

[26] *Hasidism and Modern Man,* pp. 68–69; also included in the present volume on pp. 3–5.

What?! Will someone ask whether we know our own, whether we realize it? In one of his Hasidic tales, Martin Buber gives us "the question of questions," "the query of queries." "Before his death, Rabbi Zusya said 'In the coming world, they will not ask me: "Why were you not Moses?" They will ask me: "Why were you not Zusya?" ' " [27]

What there is in the way of conversation, monologue, secret dialogue, permits of no eavesdropper and no partner. To be sure, as we read the living legend Martin Buber, we think we are constantly hearing that greeting which could be his greeting. This greeting which was once entrusted to a high messenger is now brought to the individual. Now it outlines a life and distinguishes it. There is a streaming current in this greeting, too. It goes: "Fear not!"

[27] *Tales of the Hasidim: Early Masters,* translated by Olga Mark (New York: Schocken Books, paperback edition, 1961), p. 251.

**Albrecht Goes ❦ THE "PATRIARCH"
FROM JERUSALEM**

Personal Encounters with Martin Buber[1]

WHENEVER MARTIN BUBER SPOKE AT A GERMAN UNIVERSITY DURING his visits in the 1950s, three generations felt deeply involved, each to an equal degree.

The youngest generation, the students, who could hardly know from their own experience what Jewish intellectuality means, now saw this nearly extinguished tradition bodily before them as the scholar with the high, bright forehead, the "Patriarch" from Jerusalem, stood at the lectern.

The oldest generation rejoiced at its re-encounter with the man who in the years after 1920 had shown them through his own example how adult education (what we now call "Volkshochschule" or "Volksbildungswerk") could be developed. He had shown how important it is that there be someone who has thorough knowledge in individual disciplines but at the same time knows how to establish connections with neighboring fields; who can speak in simple terms about difficult things without inappropriately simplifying the things themselves, and who finds within himself the guiding light for the whole: what

[1] A radio address by Albrecht Goes on the West German Regional Radio Network, September 29, 1962.

man's purpose is, and what, in the final analysis, each individual's effort should lead to.

We, the middle generation, sat between these two, we who in the last years of Buber's residence in Germany (before his forced exile in 1938)[2] were about to reach the age of responsibility. By this time it had reached the point where the natural structures of our society—the family, village and city, the tribal and social strata—no longer held an iota of actual security nor any promise of genuine community. It turned out (and since that time this experience has not ceased to burden our lives; 1962 is the same as 1935 in this sense) that no serious phrases could be used in common with our next-door neighbor any longer—neither "people" nor "image of man," neither "peace" nor "God." But at the same time it became apparent that there may be very remote people with whom a community does exist, passing over many a chasm—a community that is sensed, but more than that, a community which admittedly is in need of interpretation, translation, realization.

At that time when much of life that seemed to us secure abandoned us and many advisers were at a loss for counsel, Buber's books *Dialogue* and *I and Thou* were as important to us as bread; at that time words of Hasidic wisdom like "There is nothing more whole than a broken heart" instilled in us something like security in the face of all external appearance,

2 On December 21, 1962, Buber wrote to Goes from Jerusalem: "With a very special joy I have read your radio address which was sent to me in recent days. It has such a beautiful authenticity because a story is really told in it. I would like to correct a few little things because they are really not unimportant:

"I was not 'driven out.' They actually did not want to let me emigrate because I was not able to pay the 25% of the value of my Polish land which they required; only after all sorts of interventions was I allowed to spend about two-thirds of the year in Palestine under the condition that I live the remaining time in Germany and keep my house there in a 'habitable' condition—which my wife took so seriously that in November there was really something worth plundering. There is a lot more to this story which I may perhaps be able to tell you sometime."

hope where there was nothing to hope for, a pathway through a dense thicket. In those days we discovered "The Word" anew in the powerful, stark passages from Holy Writ that came out of the Buber-Rosenzweig workshop in Heppenheim and Frankfurt,[3] those raucous invocations. If the polished Luther Bible had tempted us to read rapidly, to gloss over this and that, now it hit home—the voice, not the letter: "Abend ward und Morgen ward: zweiter Tag." [Evening came and morning came: second day.] [4] And it was of no little importance to know this: the man from whom all this emanated is still among us. The lamp in Heppenheim on the Bergstrasse is still burning. We can place our little slips of paper in front of his door as the students once laid their notes at the door of the Great Maggid. And when an answer came, it directed us to the toil of everyday living, to our mannerly or unmannerly neighbor, and it read: "You shall not withhold yourself."

Then the years of total eclipse had come. But then he stood here before us, and it was a day of wish-fulfillment. Life allowed us to say "Thank you" to him who now spoke to us.

"To him who now spoke to us"—to say now a word about Martin Buber the orator: If these evenings were experiences of a special kind, it was mainly because of what this man did *not* do and what he did *not* say. I have never known anyone who was less concerned about supplying material with which to ignite the flammable part of an audience. He certainly did not say what people expected to hear, nor did he say anything that produced shock effects. His object was neither to please nor to displease his audience. But of course he also did not destroy his

---

[3] Martin Buber began his great work of translating the Hebrew Bible into German with Franz Rosenzweig (1886–1929). After Rosenzweig's death he wanted to continue the work with his son-in-law Ludwig Strauss (1892–1953). The death of Strauss (see "A Solid House" in this volume) also made this collaboration impossible, and Buber was forced to continue this work alone. After numerous revisions it was completed in 1961 (*Die Schrift* [Cologne and Olten: Jakob Hegner Verlag, 1962]).

[4] The Luther translation of Genesis 1:8 reads: "Da ward aus Abend und Morgen der andere Tag."

hearers' readiness to listen. He did not say, "The subject matter is too broad to be covered in an hour," or other boring statements of that variety. He went straight into his subject, and it appeared as if he were engaged in his own patient monologue and dialogue which was simply being continued here where thousands of people were congregated around him. He distributed with great sobriety what he once called "the bread of being together," [5] this of course in a German of great grace—what I would call the grace of Hofmannsthal [6]—not being afraid to employ words of foreign origin, but using them sparingly. Nothing esoteric could force its way in. When the listener left the lecture hall at the end of a speech, his leap back into a foolish environment (this non-world of all sorts of orators) was painful, to be sure. But there was no division such as "Here is the world; there is God." Indeed I would go so far as to say that with Buber there was not even a dichotomy between "the world" as such and "God's world." Everything was "the world," but of course a world permeated with the Song of the Hasid of Berdichev, the song that Buber loves so much: "Wherever I go: thou! Wherever I stand: thou." [7] And thus one could not fail to comprehend: There is no other pathway but the pathway that leads into this world.

A common task had then brought us together in personal encounter, and in the course of the years we had a few real dialogues, dialogues between the two of us, or, when Frau Paula Buber[8] sat together with us at tea, a dialogue for three. I took no notes on these conversations; in one sense I now find

[5] In the letter of December 21, 1962 (see note 2 above) Buber corrected Goes's use here of the German word "Mitsein," which he says should read "Selbstsein." Goes should therefore have said "the bread of being oneself."

[6] Hugo von Hofmannsthal (1874–1929), Viennese poet and dramatist who had considerable influence on the young Buber.

[7] *Tales of the Hasidim: Early Masters,* p. 212.

[8] Paula (née Winkler) Buber (1877–1958) wrote novels and essays under the pen name Georg Munk. She died in Venice while she and Martin Buber were en route from the United States to Israel. See also "A Solid House" in this volume.

this distressing. But on the other hand, in a world which has grown so unaccustomed to directness and intellectual extravagance, in a world so concerned about preserving things that it will soon make a tape recording of every family breakfast, it must be possible for two or three people to taste the joy of the moment, to open themselves, and give themselves to it, completely and without any side glance toward some sort of utilization. What one says and hears in such a back-and-forth exchange is never entirely forgotten or lost; it enters into the other person and becomes a part of the substance of his life, particularly if it acquired its initial life in such favorable circumstances.

The favorable circumstances: The man sitting across from me, exactly thirty years older than I, was in no way impeded by any signs of weakness. His eyes were clear, his hearing excellent; a soft tone of voice was just as possible as an animated outburst. His stupendous memory knew no failure, and this venerable personage hardly seemed to know what fatigue meant. On one occasion (it turned out to be a conversation of more than four hours) the younger man, shocked by his concern that he had wearied his fatherly friend beyond all propriety, stood up and mumbled an apology. "But what do you expect? A good conversation must be long—I mean, it must be possible for it to be long."

Partners in the same tempo—we know how much that means. In this instance it was the same; I would say: allegretto. It was of course not lento and not adagio. Buber, who in his eightieth year liked to speak of his basic experience as that which "transports a person in all his component parts, . . . so that . . . the storm blows through all the chambers" [9]—this Martin Buber is no man of lento. But tempo allegro and presto were not our choice either, and certainly not that nervous staccato that jumps from subject to subject. There were (and this too belongs in the real music of dialogue) pauses, periods of calm silence in which neither fears he might lose the

[9] *The Philosophy of Martin Buber*, pp. 689–690.

train of thought. There were precious little connections and back-tracking into the past. Something might be given only fragmentary reflection, then interrupted, but half an hour later one of us might bring it up again, and it seemed as if in the meantime the subject had gained new fullness below ground, as it were.

I shall try to characterize our conversation according to pairs of antonyms: spiritual-sensuous, abstract-concrete—that is a pair of antonyms. Spiritual . . . ready to dare a discussion in abstract terms, something like the students in the barn conversations in *Doktor Faustus*—that kind of thing was possible. But then came the marvelous moment of transition—from the Orient to the Occident, one might say; and the man who was astir with so much life and so much history began to tell a story.[10]

Or another pair of antonyms: lighthearted-serious. All right, lighthearted too, or: lightheartedness in the midst of seriousness. "Martin." (I can still hear Frau Paula's voice. We were sitting at tea in the hotel lobby.) "I see you're just about to pour all the sugar out of the bowl into your tea."

"Oh no, Paulchen." (This "Paulchen" sounded like—like a dialogue of fifty years.) "You get one lump of sugar, and Herr Goes gets one lump of sugar, and—I'll put all the rest of the lumps of sugar into my tea."

" 'In every sweet thing,' said the Hasidic teachers, 'HE can be reached.' " I said now—" and even in your oversweetened evening tea."

"Ah. Goes has started in on Hasidic tapestry-weaving. Do you know how Rabbi Shmelke . . ." And then a story followed which took up our playful conversation and moved on toward things of essential importance.

Two areas were touched upon in every conversation that we carried on: the time in which we lived, the concerns of our

10 At this point Goes told the story of "The Cab Driver." He later included it in a collection in a somewhat different form. It is on pp. 215–216 of this volume.—Eds.

moment in history; and the Holy Scripture on which he continued to work throughout these years. In these theological-literary discussions about Holy Scripture, I was really not prepared to hear even the New Testament texts—John's Gospel, for example—from Buber's mouth. And this he did without having to go to his desk to consult the text. From his memory he quoted from the original Greek, jumping over to Luther's German and then back to the Vulgate. . . .

The times, then—these our times. And since they cannot be understood in and of themselves, also the black years of tyranny. Neither of us—not the younger and certainly not the older man—really had any compelling desire to touch upon these terrible things. But could it have been avoided? It could not be avoided. And when my rage at the villains, the *terribles simplificateurs* of yesterday, and not only of yesterday, closed my throat tight, Buber took up the lead in the conversation like one who knows the way that leads through the gorges. I cannot say much about these particular conversations here. They belong in that realm in which one keeps silent. But I do have an idea now and then about the direction in which one must go to overcome destructive forces, to overcome them in such a way that they cannot destroy us anew from within.

Buber's own Jerusalem experiences are pertinent here as well. As long as it was at all possible, he had lived in the home of an Arab—not just lecturing about reconciliation, but living it. When the general command for evacuation came, the Bubers had to relocate so quickly into the Israeli quarter that they could not take his great library along with them. The landlord locked up the room in which it was housed. A few days later Iraqi troops came.

"Where are the Jews who lived here?"

"They're not here any longer." There was a house search.

"What's in that locked room?"

"Halt!" said the Arab landlord. "Behind this door is the great theological library of Professor Buber. You'll have to kill me if you want to enter that room."

"Well, what kind of men do you think we are? Do you think we're barbarians?" said the Iraqi captain and withdrew. . . . You will understand me when I say that that kind of report can be heard only in silent shame by a German in reflecting on November of 1938.

Then we concerned ourselves again and again with that period of time which I knew only from books, but which Buber knew from his own living memory. He talked about his contemporaries: Herzl and Hofmannsthal, Jakob Wassermann, Moritz Heimann and Leo Baeck. [11] Buber liked to characterize but he evaluated only very rarely. The eye of the observer was alert, but his heart sheltered the other person with his secret of life. This is the way, I said to myself, to gather experiences; then there is no danger of cynicism and bitterness destroying us. Whenever he could love (this I must add), he did not conceal his love even when his partner gave him a hard nut to crack. It was shortly after Hans Carossa's[12] death when we turned our conversation to this poet whom all three of us loved. We talked about the twilight into which he had fallen, and toward his justification of "Unequal Worlds." [13]

"You know," said Frau Buber, "I am from Bavaria, and I know Carossa's inner character. With us it's like this: One looks on for a while, and does nothing, and then one finds himself already in the soup."

[11] Theodor Herzl (1860–1904), journalist, novelist, dramatist, and founder of political Zionism; Hugo von Hofmannsthal, see note 6 above; Jakob Wassermann (1873–1934), novelist and essayist; Moritz Heimann (1868–1925), pen name Hans Pauli, novelist and dramatist whose position as editor for the Fischer Verlag in Berlin gave him considerable influence on the literature of his day; Leo Baeck (1873–1956), rabbi who refused to flee Nazi Germany and was one of the few survivors of the concentration camp at Theresienstadt; Baeck later lectured in London and at the Hebrew Union College in Cincinnati, Ohio.

[12] Hans Carossa (1878–1956), physician, poet, and novelist; probably best known for his novel *Der Arzt Gion* (Doctor Gion), published in 1931. See also notes 13 and 14 below.

[13] *Ungleiche Welten* (Unequal Worlds), an autobiographical work published in 1951.

"And yet on the other hand, Carossa was able to prevent a great deal of trouble," I said, "and finally he laid his whole life on the line. It was hanging on a thread—on one afternoon, one could say."

And then Buber: "A man who wrote *Eine Kindheit*[14] one must somehow hold dear regardless of the circumstances."

Literature, great literature—it was for him, when properly understood, a word beyond all discussion. Buber the man and Goethe the man carry on an imaginary dialogue. Yes, there was such a thing. But: Professor Buber interprets what the Poet Hölderlin meant—no, that did not happen. It was always this way: Hölderlin speaks, and Martin Buber listens. Here, too, it was wonderful how he effortlessly drew on his well-stocked mind and heart. "Gedächtnis-Sache des Herzens" [A matter for the heart's memory]—I have never comprehended these words of Goethe so fully as in conversation with Martin Buber. I recall the following little incident:

"I have to leave today at seven o'clock," I said. "I cannot miss that train at any price. The people of Nürtingen want to hear something about Mörike this evening."

[14] *Eine Kindheit* (A Childhood), 1922. Hans Carossa, elected against his will as a member of the Prussian Academy of Writers, was later placed under further pressure and elected to the European Association of Writers, of which he became president in 1942. Buber is probably referring to Carossa at two points in his writing without naming him specifically. In the Buber volume of *The Library of Living Philosophers* (pp. 720–721) he writes: "An important poet had allowed himself to accept an honorary office from the leading perpetrators of a communal guilt. Afterwards he grieved over it for a series of years until his death. When we had been together, some time before his death, and were taking leave of each other, he seized my arm and, obviously referring to a sentence in my book *Images of Good and Evil*, said in an unforgettable tone of voice, 'Is it not true that one cannot do evil with the whole soul?' And I confirmed it and him by saying as answer and as farewell, 'Yes.' " He is also probably referring to Carossa in the speech (quoted in the Editors' Introduction to this volume) before American psychiatrists in 1957 when he refers to "three important and, to me, dear men" who had fallen into long illnesses "from their failing to stand the test in the days of an acute community guilt." Albrecht Goes has also written an essay on Carossa, whom he visited in Passau in 1945.

"Mörike," said Buber, listening intently for a moment to the sound of the name. But then without hesitation: "The wooden utensils in the Mozart novella,[15] spoons and cutting boards which Mozart buys in Vienna—that has always been so appealing to me. It's the whole Mozart: First the playthings, but then *Don Giovanni*."

"Yes, and it's the whole Mörike: this little purchase for a loved one and then 'Ein Tännlein grünet wo . . .' " [16]

"Well, there you have something good for your lecture. . . ."

"By the way, we have, believe it or not, another cab driver story to tell," said Frau Buber on that evening. "This time in Berlin; Martin must tell about it."

"Yes, I left something in the car again, and got it back again; this time it was something rather valuable—my magnifying glass. The driver brought it into the hotel, asked for the little gentleman with the big white beard. That seemed to suffice for the bellhop in the Savoy. He could not locate me and came back three times. He wanted to hand me that thing himself. I said: 'You went to a lot of trouble.' And then he added—this time with a Berlin accent: 'Well, yes, people like me would like to do something right, too.' "

"We thought," said Frau Buber, "it was a nice story."

"Nice stories are always present in the world," I said then. "You only need a magnet to attract them. You, Herr Professor, are such a magnet."

"Good!" said Buber, and hit the table with his flat palm—I can still hear it. This "Good" did not mean: "You know how to tell a person something nice." It meant rather: "Yes, that's how things are arranged. That's an idea to pursue. One can call to life either of these: evil deeds and deeds of righteousness; that is true."

[15] Eduard Mörike, *Mozart auf der Reise nach Prag* (Mozart on his Journey to Prague), 1856. Albrecht Goes has written numerous essays on his fellow Swabian pastor and poet Eduard Mörike (1804–1875).

[16] "A little fir-tree grows green in the forest, who knows where . . ." These are the beginning lines of a poem with which Mörike ends his Mozart novella.

That's an idea to pursue: This kind of expression comes from the world of beginning; and that's actually the way it always was in these talks. One always came close to the "world of beginning." "Morgenwind umflügelt die beschattete Bucht." [The morning wind wings around the shadowed bay.] I could still point out the path in Tübingen where on the way home from a long discussion with Buber this marvelous line from Goethe flew about me like a butterfly for a long time. It was in the evening, and the evening wind was blowing, but I did not think "evening," but, rather, "morning."

And yet it would have been a dream remote from life if in each discussion with this man of a Biblical old age there had not been a consciousness of a serious "perhaps": Perhaps this is the last conversation, and every goodbye as we parted company could have meant farewell forever. But no matter how we exchanged greetings—and our greetings were never superficial—whether "Auf Wiedersehen" or "Shalom" or "Leben Sie wohl," the moment derived its life, its fleeting life, from that which is permanent: from sharing in the great task which needs fathers, sons, and grandchildren—which is the subject of a letter from Franz Rosenzweig that Martin Buber keeps in his files and in his heart:

"At any rate: The end is not our concern, but the beginning and the act of beginning are."

Albrecht Goes ❦ THE CAB DRIVER

I NEVER MET HIM, THE CAB DRIVER THAT THIS STORY IS ABOUT, but because the man who told me about his conversation with him had as direct a way of telling a story as a traveler from the East, I almost feel that I have seen that driver myself.

We were discussing the question of whether words—words, plain and simple—could produce some change in a man. We were sitting in a small boarding house over a cup of tea; the face of the old man opposite me shone toward me, and his eyes were kindly and bright. "Now I must tell you a story about a cab driver," he began.

"It happened in New York,[1] where I had to travel some distance to do an errand. It is customary to exchange a few words with one's cab driver—about the weather, perhaps—and then to keep silent. So we spoke about the weather, the buildings we were passing, and things of that sort. Suddenly the driver turned toward me and said: 'Mister, I've got something to ask you. The other day I read that you don't have to get mad at

---

[1] Albrecht Goes originally included the story of "The Cab Driver" in his radio address "The 'Patriarch' from Jerusalem." On December 21, 1962, Buber wrote to Goes: ". . . not New York, but rather Los Angeles. This is not unimportant since the man apparently belonged to the Spanish-Catholic type which is not rare in California."—Eds.

people right away. What do you think about that? Do you agree?' 'Yes,' I said, 'I think so too. But where did you read that?' 'Well, in a magazine. Don't laugh, but the guy who said that is seven hundred years old.' 'You mean, he lived seven hundred years ago?' 'Yeah, that's what I said . . . Name of Francis.' 'Francis?' 'Oh yes, Francis of Assisi.' 'Oh, then you have read something good.' And now I told my cab driver about St. Francis of Assisi. Then I got out, paid my fare, and went about my business. But soon I missed my eyeglass case and thought that the handsome case must have fallen out of my pocket in the cab. Twenty minutes later I came out of the building—and who do you suppose came walking toward me? My cab driver, with the case in his hand. Now, you have to consider that for such a driver time is money and gasoline is more money. But there he was, returning my lost item to me. So I said to him: 'Thank you. That was good of you. You are a nice man.' Whereupon something very odd happened. The driver put his arms around me and said, 'Nobody has ever said that to me.' You can imagine the strange sight: that giant of a man embracing *me,* of all people. . . . Well, that is about all I have to tell. These were words. And, do you know, perhaps I *really* got through to him with words."

This nice story is already finished. And actually, enough has been said—enough to gain confidence in words, those words which, as my companion put it, we *really* speak to another man.

Albrecht Goes ❦ A SOLID HOUSE

IT WAS ALL LIKE IN THE PREVIOUS YEAR: THE SAME APARTMENT in Tübingen which was at the Bubers' disposal during their stay in Swabia; the same setting for tea; even the same atmosphere of an early summer afternoon. The professor had his accustomed armchair; but Paula Buber's seat was occupied by daughter Eva, the widow of the poet Ludwig Strauss, who was accompanying her father on his European trip in the year after Paula Buber's death. What was missing? The aura of Munich which had been such an integral part of Paula Buber—if Munich means Baroque architecture and hobgoblin tricks, the south wind's yellow light by the Theatine Church, Karl Valentin's logic and the melancholy madonnas that seem to rise from the Victuals Market for the glory of the altar, Canaletto colors all around, and a smile seemingly floating in the air. . . .

And suddenly, I no longer know how, we were talking about their sudden farewell in Venice in August of the previous year.

Waiting for the boat which was to take them back to Israel they had stopped over in that city for two days, and with a strange impatience—so Martin Buber recalled—his wife had foregone a gondola ride to finish correcting a certain manuscript. Then the ship was ready, they occupied their cabin—and she collapsed. The ship's doctor came, examined the patient, and asked about her age. "What?! Eighty-one years old? I am sorry, but I cannot let you take the trip." So they took a gondola to the hospital on the Lido, with the patient seeming to be in a deep coma.

"I set up my papers on a table in her room," said Martin Buber. "The room was located on one of the upper floors of the hospital. When she regained consciousness, she would immediately have a view of the open sea, the area before Torcello. And so it was: Early the next day she came to: she recognized me, took a sip of tea, and then spoke one single sentence in a very clear voice. Without anything preceding or following it, she said only this: 'Platen's grave was near Syracuse.' We had hardly mentioned Platen in recent weeks."

"One never knows," I said. "I remember that last year she quoted lines from Mörike, and from Hölderlin as well. And, after all, Venice does suggest Platen: 'Venedigs Meer, Venedigs Marmorhallen/beschaun mit sehnsuchtsvoll erstaunten Sinnen.' [To view the sea and the marble halls of Venice with yearningly astonished senses.] And I wonder if it doesn't go on like this in one's semi-conscious: If it cannot be my new home, Jerusalem, that receives me—not to mention my old home— then let it be here, facing the sea, the sea that is the same in Venice and in Syracuse.

"She soon fell asleep again and did not respond when we talked to her after she had given soft moans. But suddenly she said: 'I felt quite safe on the boat. And Ludwig is such a good swimmer.' "

Could she have meant the trip from the ship to the shore? Does a soul have experiences under the cover of unconsciousness which rise from the depths days later? Or is Charon, the sure ferryman, already on board? And suddenly Ludwig is there, Ludwig Strauss, the son-in-law who has been dead for years. . . . A German writer who wrote Hebrew verse in Palestine while continuing to write in German . . . and in that sense truly a good swimmer from one shore to another.

"And then, on her last day, she said: 'Quite near by my brother has a solid house.' "

I did not comment on that. . . . But it immediately occurred to me that since the days of Abraham, Israel's sacred sorrow has been the concern about a good grave.

And as though she could read my mind, Eva said: "My mother could not have known that the Jewish cemetery of Venice is quite close to the hospital. We could only take that 'solid house' to mean a grave."

Whereupon Buber said: " 'My brother,' she said. She had no brother—not in life. But when some parting sorrow is removed from her, then the one who takes it off her soul presumably is a brother. We shall not unravel this."

Finally I said: "A solid house. . . . It made me think of Mignon's verses: 'Ich eile von der schönen Erde/Hinab in jenes feste Haus.' [I hasten from the beautiful earth/Down to that solid house.] The only difference is that what Mignon begs for—'Make me young again forever'—here belongs to silence. Not to the black silence which renounces, but to the other kind—the silence that trusts."

Martin Buber ❦ SECOND RESPONSE [1]

I LIVE A SHORT DISTANCE FROM THE CITY OF WORMS, TO WHICH I am also tied by ancestral tradition; and from time to time I visit there. When I do so, I always go first to the cathedral. It is a visible harmony of members, a whole in which no part deviates from the norm of perfection. I walk around the cathedral, gazing at it in perfect joy. Then I go to the Jewish cemetery. It consists of cracked and crooked stones without shape or direction. I enter the cemetery and look up from this disorder to the marvelous harmony of the cathedral, and it seems to me as if I were looking from Israel up to the Church. Here below there is no suggestion of form, only the stones and the ashes beneath the stones. The ashes are there, no matter how they have been scattered. The corporeality of human beings who have become ashes is there. It is there. It is there for me. It is there for me, not as corporeality within the space of this planet, but as corporeality deep in my own memories, back into the depths of history, back as far as Sinai.

[1] I.e., the last of two responses in a dialogue ("Church, State, Nation, Jewry") with Karl Ludwig Schmidt, Professor of New Testament Theology in Bonn, held in Stuttgart, January 14, 1933. This translation by William Hallo is from *Christianity: Some Non-Christian Appraisals*, edited by David W. McKain. Copyright 1964 by David W. McKain. Used by permission of the publisher, McGraw-Hill Book Company.

I have stood there; I have been united with the ashes and through them with the patriarchs. That is a remembrance of the divine-human encounter which is granted to all Jews. The perfection of the Christian God-space cannot divert me from this; nothing can divert me from the God-time of Israel.

I have stood there and I have experienced everything myself. I have experienced all the death that was before me; all the ashes, all the desolation, and all the noiseless wailings become mine. But the covenant has not been withdrawn for me. I lie on the ground, prostrate like these stones. But it has not been withdrawn for me.

The cathedral is as it is. The cemetery is as it is. But nothing has been withdrawn for us.

If the Church were more Christian, if Christians were more fulfilled, if they did not have to dispute with each other as much as they do, Karl Ludwig Schmidt holds that there would be a keener debate between Christians and ourselves.

Were Jewry once more to become Israel, were the sacred countenance to appear once more from behind the mask, then, I would counter, the separation would remain unbridged, but there would not be a more bitter argument between us and the Church, but rather something wholly different, which today is still inexpressible.

In conclusion I ask you to listen to two quotations which appear to contradict each other but do not contradict each other.

The Talmud (Yebamoth 47a) teaches:

If in this day and age a convert comes in order to be received into Judaism let him be told: "What have you seen in us, that you wish to be converted? Do you know that the people of Israel are at this time tortured, battered, buffeted, driven about, that suffering has overtaken them?" If he says: "I know, and I am not worthy," then let him at once be received.

This might seem to be Jewish arrogance. It is not. It is nothing other than the public declaration of that which cannot be dismissed. The distress is a real distress, and the disgrace is real disgrace. But there is a divine meaning in it which assures us that as God has promised us (Isaiah 54:10), he will never let us fall from his hands.

And the Midrash says (Exodus Rabba XIX, Sifra on Leviticus 18:5):

The Holy One, blessed be he, declares no creature unworthy, rather he receives every one. The gates are opened at every hour, and whoever seeks to enter, will enter. And thus He says (Isaiah 26:2): "Open ye the gates, that the righteous nation (*goy zaddik*) that keepeth faithfulness may enter in." It is not written: That priests may enter in, that Levites may enter in, that Israelites may enter in. Rather is written: That a *goy zaddik* may enter in.

The first quotation dealt with converts, but not this quotation: it deals with all mankind. The gates of God are open to all. The Christian need not go via Judaism, nor the Jew via Christianity, in order to enter in to God.

Albrecht Goes ❦ A MORNING HOUR AT WORMS

ONE DAY IN LATE FALL IT SO HAPPENED THAT I HAD AN HOUR BE-
tween trains at Worms. I had no distinct earlier memories of
the city, but I did know that the cathedral had been damaged
during the war, though fortunately not seriously; I remembered reading that it had been repaired and that religious
services were again being held there. Well, and after all, this
was Worms on the Rhine, the city of Kriemhilde, a bit of the
Nibelungenlied. So I was glad to leave the train there, asked
for directions to the cathedral, and immediately the joy which
years ago had engulfed me at the sight of the sacred citadel
returned. I saw reddish-gray walls, a bit of green moss, clear
halls, a severe construction; even the careful restoration
exuded no strangeness. The space was neither large nor small;
in that perfect way which is part of the magic of the Roman-
esque it was in harmony with living beings. It was good to be
there—that is all I can say, and yet this is saying quite a lot.

It probably was a conversation with Martin Buber years before which now made me realize that I would find another
archetypal phenomenon—if I may say so—in that town. Together with Prague, Worms is the oldest Jewish settlement
within the boundaries of the old German empire, and I had
reason to hope that I would get to see the age-old Jewish cemetery.

Has anyone thought of decorating the city official [1] through whose good offices this cemetery actually survived the terrible twelve years of destruction? Someone should consider it. As for me, I shall never forget that morning hour: the cloudy sky, the tall, defoliated acacia tree; and in the tall, soft grass the many hundreds of tombstones, black and crumbled, some of them sunken and crooked, hundreds of years old. How far do the tracks go back? Surely to the year 1300, perhaps even farther. Who rests here? Physicians, healers, Bible scholars, merchants and tradesmen; itinerants, residents and strangers; the respected and the persecuted, the difficult and the dignified; those stabbed in the night and those secretly poisoned—surely such people too. No one knows their fates any more. The Hebrew inscriptions, clearly legible, do give names and trades. What else they tell us is what exists always, across the ages and beyond our time: the blessing of Aaron and the panegyrics of the Psalms.

It is quite still. No voice is heard. The wind and the rain and the sun; the birds under the sky; the fire and smoke of wartime; and, most recently, flying squadrons—all these have passed above the stones. Now the stones themselves talk, the stones with their signs; dark moss grows in the crevices—how does it manage to get through the winter here?—and the solitary wanderer is carried along by the eternal pleas: "Give ear, O Shepherd of Israel, thou that leadest Joseph like a flock; thou that dwellest between the cherubim, shine forth."

[1] Friedrich Maria Illert, 1892–1966.—Eds.

Martin Buber ✻ THE CHILDREN [1933]

THE CHILDREN EXPERIENCE WHAT HAPPENS AND KEEP SILENT, BUT in the night they groan in their dreams, awaken, and stare into the darkness: The world has become unreliable. A child had a friend; the friend was as taken for granted as the sunlight. Now the friend suddenly looks at him strangely, the corners of his mouth mock him: Surely you didn't imagine that I really cared about you?

A child had a teacher, a certain one among all the others. He knew that this person existed, so everything was all right. Now the teacher no longer has a voice when he speaks to him. In the courtyard the space that leads to him is no longer open.

Even the beautiful landscape where a child went wandering and playing has become uncanny.

What has happened? A child knows many things, but he still doesn't know how it all fits together.

For its spirit to endure and grow, a child needs what is constant, what is dependable. There must be something there that does not fail.

The home is not enough; the world must be part of it. What has happened to this world? The familiar smile has turned into a grimace.

The child is fearful, but he can tell no one of his anxiety, not even his mother. That is not something that can be told about. He cannot ask anyone either. No one really knows why everything is the way it is.

The child is enraged, but this rage can find no outlet; it withdraws into the depths. This is a passion that cannot be allowed to flare up; it smolders and corrupts. The soul no longer has an outlet in the world; it hardens. This is how a child becomes bad.

Parents, educators, what can be done about this going to the bad, about this *ressentiment?*

I know nothing else but this: to make something unshakable visible in the child's world. Something which cannot fail because it is not subject to the vissicitudes of current history, of its lability, something that is not of this hour, but rather from before time. Something that is ours, that cannot be snatched away from us. We must make Israel something capable of being experienced by the child in its world, as something that is familiar, intimate, worthy of eternal trust. This does not mean replacing a nationalistic image of man with another nationalistic image. It does not mean to say that we are "also" a people, that we also have our way of life and our own worth. We are not a different edition of the genus "nation"; we are the only specimen of our kind. We are Israel. Having been reduced and abandoned, we have remained impervious to categorization. We are within the grasp of all the earthly powers; the conceptual categories have found us beyond grasp. I do not say this with self-assured pride; I say it with fear and trembling. This fate belongs historically to Israel—this fate of being thus entangled in the fate of the peoples and thus discharged from it: of being thrown out of it and remaining part of it in this way.

But part of Israel is also the privilege of renewing in such distress the original covenant through which it came into being. Israel is not to be revealed to the children as a substitute but rather as the true uniqueness which shapes our lives and which we have forgotten. Once again an urgent necessity has caused us to find our name again. Not as a thing to be boasted about ("We have something like that too"), not as one of the emblems on the pennants of the earth, but rather as the sign of a covenant with the rights and duties of a union. Israel means to practice community for the sake of a common covenant in which our existence is founded; to practice in actual living the community between being and being, man and man, toward which end creation was created. And today this means to preserve directness in a world which is becoming more and more indirect, in the face of the self-righteousness of collectivities to preserve the mystery of relationship, without which a people must decay in an icy death.

But have we not started out ourselves on the road toward becoming a self-righteous collectivity? May we yet expect the grace of renewing the original covenant? Is it still incumbent upon us to represent that uniqueness? Are we still capable of making that which is unshakable visible to the children? Are we still Israel? It is up to us to answer this question—not by pathos-filled explanations that prove nothing, but rather through our bearing in daily life, in the midst of its dismaying anomalies.

It is very important for us to become really aware of our basic values, of our language, and of our history; all this must enter not merely into our consciousness, but into our blood. But it is even more important for us to live as Israel, practicing community and preserving directness. Externally this has been impeded or thwarted in a thousand ways. Nevertheless, nothing must dissuade us from standing by the members of the German nation in unbroken personal integrity, without reservation and free of animosity, wherever we encounter them, in such a way that we are able to see each other and recognize one another. Even today, especially today, even though it has been made cruelly difficult for us, human openness is a dire need.

Within Jewry one would think all holds are barred. However, when I disregard all the small congregations which in these hard times have joined together and risen to the status of large families, I notice more organizational activity, even organizational inactivity, than daring personal action, more "welfare" than brotherly concern, more routine than initiative, more execution than devotion. "Who knows," said the rabbi of Berdichev about the merciless Sodomites, "perhaps they too had a community donation box where the people who were well off could drop their alms, so as not to have to look the poor in the eye!" These boxes are called "funds" today. Let nobody think he can buy his way out through a contribution! He who does not confirm directness here denies Israel.

Can we hope for a reversal, a breakthrough? I ask you who read this.

Teach your children Jewish substance, seek to form their lives in a Jewish way—but this is not enough. You must begin with yourselves. Israel is more than form and substance. It needs to be realized in our entire personal, interpersonal, communal reality.

It is up to us to make the world reliable again for the children. It depends on us whether we can say to them and to ourselves: "Don't worry. Mother is here."

Albrecht Goes ❦ NOTHING BUT TO LIVE [1959]

WHAT IS THAT IN THE BACKGROUND OF THE PICTURE ON THE FOL-
lowing page? Brambles or plantations? It could be both. It is
an Israeli landscape. Not barbed wire any more. For a moment, to be sure, one cannot keep a vision of horror from reap-
pearing in the foreground: Bergen-Belsen, Mauthausen, violence and destruction.

The mother is young. For her, the terrors of the past may
already be—just hearsay; but perhaps—think of her age!—also
a childhood memory, deeply engraved, of fear, threat, flight.
Now all around her there is the new land, the young state, a
task that demands her vital energies. She can wear a blouse
with short sleeves; there is no prisoner's number tattooed on
her skin. She appears to be gay—without bitterness. She has a
homeland; for her child, in her child. But she is a human being of this time; she knows. She has not forgotten. And even if
she could forget the past, we must not forget. For our sake. For
her sake. For the child's sake.

This child: the pretty white bib is the common property of
all children; it knows about the same hunger and the same
enjoyment of sweet pap. But there are also these hands. The
right hand is reaching for the mother's neck, for the seat of the
artery of life. And again, the memory: like this, away from their

mothers' necks, the children were torn away, at Auschwitz and elsewhere. And another thing we must not forget: There are some among us who are sorry they cannot go on raging against this people. They are isolated cases; but we have no right to take this lightly. For the sake of ten righteous men Sodom would have been spared. For the sake of ten others a people could be ruined; our German people, too.

And then there is this child's left hand, and it reaches out toward us, demanding. This serious child—what does it want? Nothing but—to live.

But what does this mean: nothing but to live? It means: to live in a world in which hatred does not beat against one from an unknown nearness or distance, perhaps from the paper one unfolds in the morning. To live in a world in which one man knows the other and really sees him.

A memory wells up: I was in secondary school, and what happened concerned me. Father used to read important texts to us after dinner; a fourteen-year-old might absorb whatever of them seemed good to him. At that time, in 1922, my father had got hold of the letter which Mathilde Rathenau wrote to the mother of her son's assassin, Frau Techow. How this sentence from her letter struck me: "If he had known my son, he would sooner have turned the murder weapon against himself than against my son." At that time, I can still remember, the thought came to me in a flash: I want to see what goes on. I want to see the other fellow the way he is. Perhaps he is quite alien to me, perhaps he is not a pleasant sort. But no idea— and all ideas have something inimical to life about them— shall prevent me from recognizing what is alive across all distances.

On the great road of graves from the centuries of persecution this people, the people of Israel among the nations, has erected the memorials of forgiveness. At present all of us, in the world of 1959, are in great danger, in mortal danger. Shall we now learn anew, together with this mother and this child, the words from Israel's ancient prayer: "Creator of the Universe, I ask nothing of you—nothing but to live"?

Martin Buber 🦌 THE END OF THE GERMAN-JEWISH SYMBIOSIS [January, 1939]

THE MOST PRONOUNCED CHARACTERISTIC OF THE HISTORY OF THE Diaspora is complete *lability*. Of course, at no hour in the history of any people is there any full security; the historical opposition of peoples and states includes the possibility of collapse at any given point of time. But stability prevails; periods of time subject to hazards and constant upheavals are followed by periods of calm construction, and regardless of whatever else may be called in question in difficult days, the nation remains in large part unaffected in its adhesion to its common heritage. In the history of our exile, on the other hand, every condition which appears to be set and permanent harbors seeds of destruction and disintegration. There is no function, no matter how important, that we perform in the economy and culture of a people, that might not from one day to the next prove to be dispensable, or even superfluous and burdensome. Every contractual alliance in history which we are convinced exists between us and a "host nation" is in reality (as is said about Frederick the Great's treaties) written on a paper with this notation in invisible writing: *sic stantibus rebus*—valid only as long as everything is as it is. But over and over again we yield to the illusion that this time it is definitive—an illu-

232

sion which, to be sure, cannot be disposed of simply with the disdainful term "assimilation," for in addition to outward adaptation there is also again and again the phenomenon of a genuine, well-developed bond with a soil and a culture—an essentially problematical but existential synthesis, one that reaches down to the depths of our existence and whose end is the rupture of an organic connection. The most remarkable and significant case of this kind has been the development of German Jewry since its emancipation, which has now been terminated through the intervention of the "host nation" (or more accurately, of the "host state")—an intervention which in the automatic thoroughness of its act of extermination, its calculated frenzy, appears quite strange in the history of western man in the twentieth century of the Christian era.

I have said that it was the most remarkable and significant case. For the symbiosis of the German and Jewish spirit as I experienced it in the four decades I spent in Germany was the first and only one since the Spanish period that received the highest confirmation that history has imparted—confirmation through *fruitfulness*. There are two kinds of encounters between two national elements which are strangers to each other: either they are strangers in a negative sense—each has no effect upon the other; they do not blend but remain distinct entities until the one who is physically weaker perishes. Or they are strangers in a positive sense: In all of their strangeness they are essentially designed for each other, oriented toward and dependent on each other. An area of common concern comes to light in which fruitful contact between them results; a cultural creation springs up which, without this encounter, would have remained uncreated. *Greco-Jewish* culture had produced only a few individual figures and works, and these only in the area of philosophy. *Spanish-Jewish* culture was rich and multifarious, but it was in its origin and decisive development an *Arabic-Jewish* culture, and had therefore come about not as an encounter between two peoples who were strangers to each other, but rather between two related peoples. The short productivity of the *German-Jewish* encounter, which had already been foreshadowed when Goethe was gripped by Spinoza's spirit, or even when Luther was gripped by the spirit of the Hebrew Bible, but whose flowering lasted hardly half a century, was a genuine and natural one. There was, to be sure, a premature and spurious acceptance of German values and German forms by Jews, an illegitimate and destructive influence of Jews on German life and culture, but this was only disconnected and peripheral, though conspicuous. In its essence the Jewish share in the German economy, society, science and art was constructive and educative. There is no area of German existence in this age in which Jewish people have not had a leading part in establishing values, setting things in order, interpreting, teaching, shaping. It was not a parasitic existence; their whole humanity was put to the task, and it bore its fruit. But even more deeply than by individual accomplishment the symbiosis is verified by a striking collaboration between the German and the Jewish spirit. Whether German poetry like that of Stefan George is transformed by Jewish disciples into a historical and cultural phenomenon, or whether the ideas of a Jewish thinker like Edmund Husserl are added by German disciples to the methodological fundamentals of various branches of knowledge—we always observe the phenomenon not just of areas which complement each other, but rather of a genuine fructification. I myself have, in intellectual association with Germans of prominence, experienced again and again how out of the depths common ground was unexpectedly ploughed up and became shared words and symbols.

In the face of such a reality it is understandable that many a Jewish man gave himself over to all that is German with entirely too little restraint. My colleagues and I have warned of this loudly and untiringly in all these years, but that reality was in most cases stronger than we were. Anyone who makes a casual judgment here has not understood the tragic character of fate in the Diaspora, the origin and annihilation of genuine syntheses.

I do not wish to speak here of powers and the powerlessness that have brought on the catastrophe, which, like none other before it, proffers an image of the rupture of an organic context. It means a deeper rupture in the German spirit itself than can be imagined today. A year before the rupture, a German thinker (Paul Tillich) pointed to this impending danger in his speech commemorating Hegel: "The Jewish principle," he said, and this he understood to mean the *prophetic* principle of the intellect, "has become our own fate and a 'secessio judaica' would be a separation from our own selves." Today the continuity of development in German intellectual life is cut off. If it is ever resumed again, it will of necessity reestablish its ties with those values which supported the symbiosis, and with those works which resulted from it. But the symbiosis itself is terminated and cannot return.

The Jews who have escaped from German soil here onto Jewish ground and (this is our hope and expectation) who will yet escape here bring an important contribution to the construction of our life and our community in the form of the great strengths and values which they have absorbed and woven together with the fabric of their Jewish being in the symbiosis. Our settlement too is a melting pot, but not one into which, like the American melting pot, various kinds of metal are haphazardly thrown together, but rather one in which various alloys of the same primal metal are brought together. Every one of them donates to the homeland a different precious commodity from the world of nations. Here all of this is to be smelted together into a great form of life. The contribution of German Jews must be especially valuable and welcome to us. Embedded in Jewish substance they bring to us something of that noble element of the German soul which is being denied and stifled by their tormentors.

Martin Buber 🦋 THEY AND WE   [November, 1939]

On the first anniversary of the "Kristallnacht" [1]

WHAT HAPPENED A YEAR AGO IN GERMANY WILL BE PRESERVED IN the annals of history as one of the most ghastly examples of the treason of a state. The term "treason" is used with respect to relations between the state and its citizens only in the sense of treason from the lower level to the top. One speaks of treason by treasonable citizens, of their betrayal of the state. But the worst treason of this kind cannot be so pregnant with evil as that which the state commits against a part of its citizens. Whenever any state banishes from the area of its protection and responsibility one of its minorities, the one which is the most conspicuous, and annihilates it slowly or quickly, as Germany has done with its Jews, without this minority having transgressed against it—in so doing such a state shakes the foundations of its own existence. For a state cannot exist when its citizens have no confidence that it will continue to be loyal to them as they are loyal to it. Even though the Germans may have soothed themselves either yesterday or today by saying that all those who have been persecuted and killed, whose

1 Anti-Semitic riots organized by the Nazis on November 9 and 10, 1938, the "night of broken glass."—Eds.

shrines have been defiled and destroyed, are only Jews, the Jews who obtained their equal rights only a few generations ago, the hearts of all men who do not belong to the tribe of the thugs and their masters must be heavy; and these men must steel themselves for the fact that after this national minority another minority will come to the fore—a religious one or a social one; and when this has come to pass, then the very heart of the state will be corroded. This regime must collapse, and if it does not collapse soon, if this monster cannot be overcome very quickly, if this lack of confidence spreads, then the population will lose its desire to serve the state.

I speak intentionally of the German *state,* that is to say, of the organization which the German people have established, or with which they concur, or of the rulers whom the people have installed or whom they tolerate, not of the German people themselves. What happened in Germany a year ago was not an outbreak of a nation's passion, of widespread Jew-hatred, nor was it so in any action committed against us in these seven years. It was a command from the upper level and was executed with the precision of a dependable machine. For two weeks during the preparation of the Nuremberg Laws, school children came by the windows of my house in Heppenheim every morning at six o'clock and sang the pretty song "Only when the Jew's blood squirts from the knife." In this way a command which had been given was carried out. On the next morning we waited in vain for the procession. In Poland I saw what elementary Jew-hate is—an outbreak of instinctual drives; I have never seen it in Germany. It is no special problem that the apparatus operates according to plan against the Jews; it had already been like this in other instances. Perhaps it is an old habit of the German people to obey those in power, for the fact that they hold the rudder of state is proof that they are confirmed by history, that they are God-sent; it is apparently quite difficult for a German to distinguish between God and success and to imagine a God who does not go forth with strong battalions, but rather dwells "among the bruised and downcast" (Isaiah 57:15). Even some of the true intellectuals in Germany gave me the impression that they, because of an isolation natural to them and their incapacity for public action, are inclined to believe in everyone who takes over the business of politics and carries it by force with uninhibited harshness. But in the case of the Jews, something else is added to this which presents a special problem and is commonly instructive for us: It is the inner attitude of many of those who have kept up their relationships to Jews and have helped persecuted and suffering Jews. When one communicates with them, one sees that in many instances they do have a good humanitarian feeling of sympathy for those who have been declared outlaws, but that they are also not lacking in understanding of the motives of the persecutors. Of course they regret the gross form of the expulsion which they would like to attenuate, but inwardly they are in agreement with the basic tendency. We cannot dispose of this important fact with the explanation that a disease has befallen the German people, and that with their recuperation everything will be back on the right track. This is a fatuous illusion, the way an immature mind judges historical reality. Of course the German people are suffering from a serious illness; their present enemies share in the blame for this illness, but with their recuperation everything will not be back on the right track at all. And one cause among others is the fact that even earlier, before the people fell ill, things had not been running on the right track. Here we must recognize the serious problems which I feel obligated to point out today—precisely because I know and declare from time to time that a great and genuine union existed between the German and the Jewish spirit, a union which was confirmed by genuine fruitfulness. Only when we consider the cluster of problems that was peculiar to this union, when we consider it without sparing ourselves, will we learn what there is to learn from this chapter of Jewish history that is now concluded.

Out of ignorance we are in the habit of seeing the anti-

Semitism after the emancipation as a simple continuation of
and return to the anti-Semitism before the emancipation,
which was based mainly on religious feelings. But the former
was the result of strangeness and the latter the result of contact; in the former, as Pinsker put it, people hated something
like a ghost which was horrifying and incomprehensible, but
in the latter case they hated living human beings whom they
already knew to some degree. To be sure, the ghost-like feelings toward the objects of hatred had not yet been overcome,
but the ghost now had received a body. I have said "hatred";
but in reality I only rarely met men in Germany who hated
Jews. On the other hand, I often met the sort who were suspicious of the Jews.

What was it that affected them in such a way?

I would like to limit my words about this matter to an area
which is the framework in the life of the people, the area of
economics. But what is true with reference to this area is, with
certain changes, also true of the other, higher areas of life. It is
well known that the problematical Jewish relationship to the
economics of the ruling nations is a consequence of the fact
that the Jews' participation usually does not begin with the
foundation of the house but rather with the second floor. They
have no share, or only a very minor one, in the basic production, in the laborious gathering of raw materials, the hard work
on the soil in agriculture as well as mining. As artisans who
process the raw materials they usually prefer the lighter, seden-
tary occupations. To industry they supply technicians, engi-
neers and directors, and they keep away from the hard work
at machines. As I have heard with considerable concern, this
situation has not changed much even in the Soviet Russian
economy. But it is a basic characteristic of the life of all modern
people, an unexpressed and legitimate characteristic, that the
growth and fruitfulness of life can only be attained by a con-
sistent, large-scale national sacrifice, through untiring application of a people's energies to the production and processing of
raw materials. The sons of these working classes who rise up

into the intellectual professions are to a certain extent a self-renewing symbol of this process. If, then, a part of the population which stands out almost everywhere in its physical type and its peculiar movements does not participate in this national sacrifice—even though the causes of this fact are rooted in prior history—but demands a full share, and even one which exceeds its percentage in the general population, of the fruits of this sacrifice in the intellectual life and work of the people; if they join the sons of the bearers of sacrifice in droves and even push them from their places—then the soil is prepared for a new anti-Semitism. It breaks out when an economic crisis gives occasion for it, when the reward of the people's sacrifice is greatly reduced, when the rise of their sons is impeded, and especially when through unemployment something much more difficult is imposed upon broad segments of the people than that sacrifice—namely, a purposeless, hopeless life. The Jews, who stand out in the upper stories, actually or apparently unaffected by all this, become even more conspicuous than before, and in the hearts of those who were affected the impression is transformed into deep bitterness which can be compared to explosives; then a political catchword is added like an incendiary spark.

Those who threw the spark into the powder keg will not escape judgment. But we are not fulfilling our duty by mourning and complaining. We must learn from what has happened and transform what we have learned into action. The powerful cause to which we have addressed ourselves in Palestine, and which cannot be compared with any other in history, has no other meaning and will have no other substance than this: that we are finally building for ourselves a real house of our own, and in such a manner as one builds a house that is to last for a long time, that is to say, on solid and strong foundations. And the house of the people has no other foundation than that of the services of the broad ranks who carry the society in the production and processing of raw materials. We must purchase intellectual life for ourselves through the sacrifice of hard work on the soil and its products. We shall not attain any genuine culture if we build the substructure only carelessly in order to move quickly into the magnificent upper stories; if we did that, everything would collapse. Every intellectual work is born legitimately only out of the fullness of life that springs from the heavy physical work of the people; everything else is artificial and transitory. Anyone among us who cannot share in sacrificial work must feel at every hour and in every situation that he is a close associate of the workers. He must realize this: This work is my affair; only through it does my life gain foundation and security; without it I would be hanging in the air; I have no other real ground under my feet besides that which my laboring brother is gaining for me through his effort. It is very sad to see that even in this land that we call our land the veneration of the upper stories is spreading; this worship casts only a quick glance downward and then directs its eye upward with enthusiasm. This is Diaspora on the soil of Zion. What can be called a people, a genuine, unified people, can be attained in no other way than through the spirit surrounding labor in a circle of love.

If we succeed in this change of perspectives, this revaluation of values, this unified construction of public life from the bottom to the top, then an influence will be transmitted from here to the Diaspora and its relationships to the ruling peoples, and the strength and depth of that influence cannot presently be perceived.

Still more important than this is another doctrine, even though they are basically one and the same. It is directed against a false doctrine which is prevalent among us and which can be formulated in approximately this manner: The extreme and total national egotism now reigning in Germany is right in and of itself. It is the right policy for a nation, and especially in times of crisis. It seems negative to us only because it is directed against us. The most important criterion for us is that of our national egotism. Among all the horrors of assimilation I know no view in which Jews so degrade themselves as in this one, which presumes to be a result of Zionism. For thousands of years we subscribed to the doctrine that the world is founded on justice, on justice between man and man, between nation and nation. We said to ourselves and to the world: The image of history that ascribes victory and power to the transgressor is deceiving, for inwardly his victory is defeat and his power, weakness. And then we encounter in this hour the caricature of injustice, the grimace of ice-cold baseness, of a cruelty that functions like a machine, a golem on whose brow the name of Satan is inscribed; he seizes our communities one after the other, desecrates and destroys our communities one after the other. And after all this, people abound among us who say: "This messenger of Satan does bring us harm, but Satan himself is right, Satan is the true God, there is no other God but him!" After all that, people abound among us who teach: As long as we were weak, we said what we did because we were weak; but now we must become strong and do the work of Satan like the strong ones so that it may go well for us on the soil. If we accept this doctrine, we sign the indictment against us with our own hands. And this land—that it cannot be built upon injustice is attested to by its whole history. Whoever does not want to admit this truth, whoever thinks this land is like all lands, just as in his opinion we are a people like all people; to whomever the words about the Holy Land like those about the People of God are an outmoded figure of speech—he acts in the land of Israel like Hitler, for he wants us to serve Hitler's god after a Hebrew name has been conferred upon him. And whoever acts like Hitler will meet his downfall along with him. We must fight him by annihilating his idols. We must combat the realm of sacrilege by combating the sacrilege.

Can we combat it? We can combat it by setting up the Kingdom of the God of Justice in this land. How can we do this? By leading a just life. Can one begin that in this hour? There is no hour that would be more suited to it than this one. "God wages war against Amelech." We can triumph only if we carry on our war as God's war. On the present warfront, on which those who fight against Hitler know only what they are fighting *against,* but not what they are fighting *for,* God's truth is not to be found. But it is to be found here—if only we dare to serve it.

Martin Buber ✡ SILENCE AND OUTCRY [1] [Spring, 1944]

NEVER BEFORE HAVE I BEEN SO AWARE OF HOW DUBIOUS ALL OUR spiritual existence is—in spite of all the works of renewal—as in these days when the masses of our people have been abandoned to the violence of their worst enemies.

Of course we do not know the actual extent of the catastrophe as yet. Nevertheless, there is no doubt that it is immeasurably greater than any other in our history. The Jewish community in this country [Palestine], which may consider itself externally secure, is certainly not taking an attitude of indifference toward it, but there is no genuine identification. Everyone who has or had relatives or friends there feels directly affected in some way by what is happening there. All of us together do not feel it in its totality. We are lacking a collective power of imagination—the capacity to realize in common the reality "there." People are saying that it is better this way, for anyone who imagined what is taking place could not simply carry on his life. This is true, but it does not mean that it is not our duty to display an adequate amount of imagination. It is certainly not appropriate for us just to carry on our

[1] This critical statement should not be taken as evidence of an anti-Zionist attitude on Buber's part. Buber was, on the contrary, a leading spiritual Zionist.

lives; it is appropriate for us to weave whatever happens into the fabric of our lives—not in order to emit the customary roar of revenge in which the tension is relieved, but rather in order to be effective, to co-operate where it is possible to do something. But when we ask ourselves the question about what is to be done, the question as to what may be saved, our doubts become even graver. The history of the attitude of the Jewish settlement toward the catastrophe of the Diaspora begins with something that cannot be explained and cannot be understood: with silence. For days and months—so we have heard, and it has not been disputed—the well-informed knew what was happening and what plot was being hatched and kept what they knew secret from the community in the country. I do not understand that—and it cannot be understood. It is maintained that the spirit of the community at that time, as a consequence of the occasional insecurity of its own situation, was too sensitive to be concerned with the realities of the Diaspora. That is how one conducts oneself with reference to children and sick people. And who knows whether things were not left undone at that time which could have been done then and only then if the community had given all its energies to the matter? We will certainly not be able to make any exact determination about this in the near future. But the most incomprehensible thing in my eyes is this: When the community heard what was going on, and heard that it had been kept secret from it for days and months, it kept silent.

After the silence came the outcry. It was partly a spontaneous outcry and partly organized screaming. In a period of propaganda there can be no objection to the latter, for it is not possible to attempt a far-ranging rescue action without the help of the great powers involved, and for this reason it must be brought to their attention. In some cases this is, to our great sorrow, possible only when one organizes what is spontaneous; and under these circumstances it is natural that one pushes the spontaneity a bit further. The matter does not become problematical until the political note is mixed in with the outcry.

The "political note" means that one wants to exercise "pressure" through the outcry in order to obtain something which apparently is otherwise not attainable—something which, to be sure, under the given circumstances is closely connected with the intention of rescue but is by no means identical with it. From a moral viewpoint one can raise the objection that the catastrophe and the rescue are being used as a means to an end, be it an ever so important end. What this means from a moral standpoint can be made quite clear by imagining a parallel case from the life of an individual, for example a burning house or a person drowning. A person who knows no imperative more sublime than the political imperative will counter this objection by saying that there is no imperative more sublime. However, the moment we enter the exclusively political area we inescapably face the questions of utility, benefit and damage. And here it is necessary to fulfill the first condition of all political action: to shake off all pleasant illusions, for the effectiveness of illusion is a false and destructive effectiveness. In this context that means this: Firstly, it is our duty to recognize, without being limited by any illusion, that there are political notes whose audibility is unpleasant to the powers that be, and if they should become audible, they should at least not sink in. But that would still not be so bad, for one generally assumes that in the sphere of democracy there is an opportunity to appeal to public opinion against the powers in question. But this too is an illusion, for, as is well known, the task of public opinion in time of war is limited in some respects, and in cases of this type it carries practically no weight. We know this quite well, to be sure, but we do not want to recognize it when it applies to ourselves. And it is evident from all this that the person who does not want to hear the political note also turns a deaf ear toward the outcry itself of which it is a part. And if one asks such a person, he will say that the outcry is nothing but a means to a political end. In other words: The powers involved to whom we wish to appeal for rescue do not view this as help independent of the political motivation of which they disapprove. Furthermore, this has the result that what is supposed to serve the rescue does it harm.

This whole problem becomes even greater when this cause is used not only for the political purpose common to us all, but rather for the purpose of a particular party. There are parties which need the seething spirit of a nation in order to boil their brew. Their best opportunity, and sometimes their only one, is a radicalizing of the situation. They are ready to sacrifice the rescue to this opportunity. For they are clever enough to know that the "pressure methods" they have suggested are not designed to advance the rescue, but, rather, the radicalization. And only here does the really horrifying thing happen: the exploitation of our catastrophe. What sets the pace here is no longer the will to rescue, but instead the will to exploit. And they want to make even those of us who belong to no party, who are anxious to rescue what can still be rescued, subservient to a party purpose with the watchword of rescue. I have sometimes wondered whether a front could be formed in some extraordinary hour which might cut across all party lines—the front of those who want the salvation of their people with all the truth of their hearts and who want to work together for the decisive cause without consideration for the diversities of the political programs in all other questions. The splitting of the parties is a grave fact that one cannot remove from public life at present, but it is desirable to set a limit to it. The setting of this limit in an extraordinary hour, however—a limitation which must be made by individuals from all the parties—demands a purity of feeling and service which is apparently even rarer than I assumed in thinking over the possibility of cooperation. But if it should nevertheless be realized, it will look different from those talks about rescue in which I have participated.

Well then? If you ask me at this late hour what we ought to do, I have no answer other than this cruelly sober one: to save as many Jews as is at all possible; to bring them here or take them to other places; to save them by fully realistic treatment

248   MEN OF DIALOGUE

of the various practical questions with all manner of means at our disposal, wherever and whenever there is still something to be saved. Nothing of the spirit of partisanship, of politicizing, must be allowed to be part of this operation, nothing aside from the lives of the nameless ones who are to be saved. A situation may be foreseen in which even such an action will no longer be possible; one cannot predict when this will come about, but all developments point to it. Now is a time for keeping silent and for working.

Albrecht Goes 🎔 THE *DELUXE* DRESS MATERIAL

WE WERE TALKING ABOUT PROPHECY. IT IS NOT SO MUCH A FORE-
telling of details as a presentiment of what is to come. In this
sense it has been part of Israel, including that hidden Israel
which, in the days when there still was an Israel among us,
sometimes came close to us, albeit not very close. After all, the
stature of prophetic life always involves something unap-
proachable.

I had told the story of a wealthy Polish magnate, old Solomon B., who was visited by his grandson. That was in 1925,
and Herr Hitler was still quite far outside the gates. An expen-
sive piece of cloth was on the table, a heavy piece of brocade,
and the eyes of the grandson's beautiful young wife looked it
over as only a woman's eyes can look at brocade. It was dark in
the room, and the glow of the great golden seven-branched
candelabrum was dim. "A nice piece of cloth, eh?" said the old
man suddenly. "Take it along, little one, take it with you!
You'll be able to use it—for a beggar's bag. . . ." Later the
grandson said that he had never been able to forget that evening hour or the sad laughter of the old man who himself died
as a beggar.

Then an old lady said: "I too know a story about a heavy
material." She did not look at us as she told her story; I could

well imagine where her eyes were looking. . . . Then, too, she spoke in a somewhat emotional tone of voice, and I could see that the doctor—the youngest in our party—had to smile a bit at first. But then none of us smiled any more, for what the lady was telling us seemed to be out of a book of legends; and yet it was actual history, something that had happened in 1939, just a few weeks before the outbreak of the Second World War.

"It was in Breslau," so the lady said, "and I felt like having a really good, elegant dress made for myself. I went to the best dry-goods shop in town, one that used to be Jewish property. The former owner, so people said, still had some job in the store. I told the salesman what I wanted, and he tried to serve me, bringing in the most beautiful silks and velvets. But suddenly the former proprietor, a little old hunchback, was standing before me; I have no idea how he had emerged from the back of the store just like that. With one movement of his hand he brushed all those treasures aside, took a heavy *deluxe* material from the shelf, and said: 'Madam, take this one. I am telling you: You'll remember the little old man in Breslau who once recommended this material to you.'

"All at once I was in a strange quandary. I certainly had no desire to wear a heavy dress again, something that I had repeatedly done in those years; as I have said, I really felt like having a dressy dress. But the old man's mode of expression, his strange imploring tone of voice, swayed me, and so I said, after thinking it over for a few moments: 'All right, all right. Wrap up some of this material for me—how much do I need? And the trimmings, too.'

"They cut the material for me, rolled everything up, and I left the shop with the package under my arm. The old man stood by the door, and as he said good-bye to me, he used almost the same words as before, in the identical tone of voice: '. . . And you'll remember the little old man in Breslau who recommended this material to you.'

"Six years went by. One day there was one of those big air raids on Vienna. In the middle of the night and in a great hurry we had to pack our things; the servant girl cupped her hand around the candle so that no light should be visible outside. I stood before my wardrobe and hunted for what I needed the most. And then I took out none of the pretty light dresses but the one made of the heavy *deluxe* material, and I could hear a voice as if from afar: 'And you'll remember the little old man in Breslau . . .' "

Albrecht Goes ❦ JUDGMENT AND PREJUDICE

WE SOMETIMES ASK OURSELVES: IS NOT THE HISTORY OF THE MIS-understandings in our life (and here I mean life in small circles as well as large communities) to a considerable extent the history of our prejudices and not that of our dissimilarities?

And if that is so, what is the concrete form of the task we have been given—namely, the overcoming of these prejudices? What strength of insight, what imagination of the soul are required of us so that we may leave the thicket of prejudice and step into the clear world of judgment, the bright realm called "trust in the stranger"?

[1]

JUDGMENT AND PREJUDICE. . . . PREJUDICE IS THE UNMANNERLY stepbrother of judgment.

Prejudice is quick, judgment is slow; prejudice is narrow, judgment is broad. Prejudice generalizes, judgment specializes. Prejudice is inaccurate, judgment is accurate, and because it is accurate and conscientious, it bears the marks of shyness, of reserve, and probably even of weakness. Judgment knows itself, the problems it poses to itself, and yet it cannot be seduced to come to terms with that insolent haste which is the comfortable domain of prejudice. Judgment is educated; prejudice is semi-educated. And as we say this, we are immediately reminded of all the misfortune which the upsetting force of semi-education has brought upon us.

We think of the political area because, working from without to within, it has had such an influence upon our *Weltanschauung* and our style of life. One after the other, we think of the hectic, ill-considered marginalia of Wilhelm II which were able to assume importance because they came from an emperor; of the diverse specialized knowledge which the great destroyer[1] displayed and with which, mysteriously enough, he managed to dazzle and corrupt many a capable man with whom he came in contact; of the "terrible simplifiers" who control so many areas even today.

We have allowed them to lead and mislead us, we have let dreary commonplaces and evil catchwords hold sway over our thinking. One such catchword was "Polnische Wirtschaft" [a Polish mess]; another was "Das perfide Albion" [perfidious England]; a third, "Der bolschewistische Untermensch [Bolshevist subhumans]. "Der Jude," "Die Juden" [a Jew, Jews]: Such words gained currency among us and became ingrained in our consciousness—catchphrases of a generalization which does not exist.

We know—and let us ponder what we know—that a Jewish physicist and a Chinese physicist communicate with each other more easily than a Jewish physicist and a Jewish orange picker from Africa can communicate in Israel. How do our prejudices go? Here is one: "The Jews cling to money; they handle money in a special way, one that is alien to us." Anyone who utters such a sentence ought to consider what it means that for centuries we barred the Jews, the guest people within our nation, from almost all professions and let them handle only money matters, banking transactions, and deals involving interest—

[1] Hitler.—Eds.

which means that we forced them to develop and overdevelop their talent for these tasks. And we ought to consider further that in today's State of Israel Jews manage with unique determination to counteract the demonism of money in the magnificent *kibbutzim,* the collective settlements. "They are players with words, pettifoggers, analysts"—this is another statement about them, and it is as quickly said as it is inaccurate. This statement would have to read "They are the people of the word" if it were subjected to the patience of judgment. They, they alone among the nations with idols and magic forces, were entrusted with one imageless thing, the revealed word, and to it they have entrusted themselves. And since they were not invited to participate in the history of Western civilization until very late—in Germany, this invitation was issued only two hundred years ago, in the age of Lessing—is it any wonder that they entered with some impatience, with oversensitive, long-sharpened minds, with arrows of Heinrich Heine's unerring aim, with an inexorability which brooks no nebulousness and disturbs dreams?

However this may be, in this connection we shall not speak of the great guilt which we have incurred through this generalization and the evil course which ensued. We shall merely ask ourselves whether the sad obstinacy with which we keep searching for a whipping boy for our prejudices has not taken us, and does not continue to take us, into a fresh thicket. There is class prejudice—against teachers, clergymen, businessmen, the Prussians (who really no longer exist!), drivers, pedestrians, the notorious "Halbstarke" [juvenile delinquents], the Communists, and on and on.

[2]

THE THICKET OF PREJUDICE. . . . HOW CAN WE GET OUT OF IT?
To my mind, the only way is to face our prejudices in an hour

of sincere self-examination the way one faces an adversary in a duel—each man facing his own. Anyone who has been fortunate enough to have grown up in an environment of great openness, directness, and freedom will have to look for "his partner" longer; but he, too, will find one, even though at first this partner may seem quite strange to him.

What is required is an effort of patient understanding, efforts to recognize the realities of our situation. "That goes without saying," someone may say. It does not go without saying. It happens extremely seldom that a man can really recognize facts and tell about them calmly, clearly, and openly.

To see a man the way he is means much more than seeing a person now, here, and today, at a certain spot. It means to see him with his yesterdays, his origins, his childhood, his development, his country, his fate, his victories and defeats, in addition to his present life, his positive and his negative aspects, his dicta and contradictions, his tomorrows, with his future glimpsed at least in outline.

As we say this, it already becomes apparent that what is required is more than the power of understanding. The hard, laborious road that leads from prejudice to judgment demands strength of heart and imagination of soul.

I shall name three tasks that the heart has to perform. First and foremost, there is the initial decision without which, so it seems to me, there can be no way into the open. I mean the decision made entirely within a person, without witnesses, in the still of night—the decision "for" (perhaps I may call it a "primal pro") which says: I shall no longer lend my hand to the sad pursuit of building higher walls of mistrust. I cannot "embrace the millions," [2] nor can I pretend that all is harmony, but I shall strive to understand the stranger, the man whose substance differs from mine, as *the Other*. He is the Other—at present still "the Other who disturbs me," but soon he could be "the Other who completes me."

[2] A reference to "Seid umschlungen, Millionen," a line from Schiller's *Ode to Joy*.

Further: I shall not permit myself dreams about man. Dream images have no value; they are false. But I shall see my task before me: To recognize the potential in men; to complete what is suggested, to elaborate what has been sketched. Whatever I bring within the sphere of my confidence is given life by me. All of pedagogy is connected with the creative power of overrating and overtaxing—not too much, just a bit—a life that is in one's care.

And this, too: It is an exercise of the prudent mind to take objective things objectively and personal things personally. But a higher kind of venture is the ability to look away from the questionable person, or to see through him and get at the unambiguous, or at least the brighter, cause, and then to lend to this cause personal love, life, warmth, charm, and humor. He who brings to bear on the cause less than what is really personal will not loosen what has so badly hardened or sweeten what has become so bitter.

[3]

BUT WHAT IS THE POINT IN ALL THIS? WHY IS IT IMPORTANT TO find the road from the shrubbery into the open, to the bright land called "trust in the stranger"?

The answer is this: Because all of us are in danger of having our hearts harden. We are threatened with a situation in which we no longer reach the Other, in which no current of dialogue, no redeeming sign is possible any longer, in which we ourselves become unfruitful—without a heaven to warm us or an earth to nourish us . . . devoid of all directness.

Let us not misunderstand one another: Trust in a stranger is hard; like all trust, it is a "trust despite. . . ."; it is always something like a rope that is stretched over an abyss. Every day we shall have to spell it out anew: "I would rather bestow my trust in vain than choke in mistrust; I want to do it for my own sake and for the sake of the 'Holy Spirit of Life.' " I know that not *all* steps can be taken, but this does not lead me to the conclusion that *no* step is possible. With one step that is possible I shall escape the tangled world called prejudice—in one bit, in one hour.

It is true: I cannot count on power, victory, or success. As I recognize the relative rights of the Other, my judgment becomes more reserved; my "striking power" becomes reduced—that much is certain. But I have not been called as a robber or a killer, but, rather, as a builder—associated with that "occupation", that patient toil, which is mentioned in Schiller's great poem *Die Ideale:*

> Beschäftigung, die nie ermattet,
> Die langsam schafft, doch nie zerstört,
> Die zu dem Bau der Ewigkeiten
> Zwar Sandkorn nur zu Sandkorn reicht,
> Doch von der grossen Schuld der Zeiten
> Minuten, Tage, Jahre streicht.[3]

Minutes, days, years. . . . The years we shall leave to Eternal Wisdom, Love Eternal. But the minutes are our concern.

[3] Occupation which never tires, which slowly creates but never destroys, which, to be sure, only supplies grains of sand for the building of eternity, but which strikes minutes, days, and years from the great debt of the ages.

Albrecht Goes ❦ GO, SUFFER, WAIT:
THREE GIFTS FROM ISRAEL

An Address Given in Hamburg on March 11, 1962

[1]

OUTSIDE THE DOOR STANDS A MAN AND LISTENS TO THE REHEARSAL of a chamber orchestra. He knows the work that is being played inside, and they are playing it correctly, in the proper tempo and with the indicated volume of sound. And yet something is lacking. What is it? The listener in front of the door waits and examines, and now he recognizes that some instruments are missing; there are no woodwinds. Thus it is the work of music and yet it is not.

For a long time I have been like this man when I reflect about something which has been close to my heart for years: the German-Jewish and the Christian-Jewish encounter which is embodied in the societies for Christian-Jewish collaboration and which, during Brotherhood Week, has to contend with an indifferent milieu and the indolence of the human heart. Some instruments—if I may put it that way—are properly represented; the roots are in plain view. Thoughts of mourning, the consciousness of shame—these are all there. The concrete question "What can we do?" is indeed asked and an answer is

258

striven for. But I have often missed one tone—the one of *joy*.

We all know that anti-Semitism is not a *Weltanschauung* or a way of life but a plague; one has to be against it the way one is against the plague—unequivocally and without any ifs, ands or buts. But any "anti-anti" is inadequate, if not downright unproductive. Those of us who occasionally go to hear lectures will be in heartfelt agreement with Goethe's request that anyone who wanted to speak to him ought to tell him something positive, for he was full of problems himself. The tone of joy with which I am specifically concerned here, a tone which has seldom enough been clearly audible, is surely at home in Israel. The Book of Psalms—the *Buch der Preisungen* [Book of Praises], as Martin Buber has called it—is powerful testimony that joy is as much part of Israel as the grain, the lilies of the field, the Temple—and in still other ways; and the "roaring enthusiasm" of Hasidic chants, the danced joy in God which took hold of Franz Rosenzweig in Eastern lands as late as 1918, is still alive—even in the world of doom in Anne Frank's hiding place in Amsterdam. You will remember the end of an act in the dramatization of *The Diary of Anne Frank:* at the beginning of the festival of Hanukah these people, even they, have to sing. To be sure, for all of us who view and ponder things seriously and consciously it is not easy but hard to attain joy. I am now 54 years of age, and my thoughts go back exactly 40 years to a June day in 1922—it seems like only yesterday—to the shots which hit Walther Rathenau in Berlin. The minds that were startled by these shots were destined not to regain their tranquility. We cannot travel to Hamburg without thinking of Bergen-Belsen, which is on the way, and in recent years men like Zind, Stielau and so many others have seen to it in their fashion that none of us takes an illicit rest. But as far as the survivors among the people of Israel are concerned, the voice of Margarete Susman—who was born in Hamburg and now lives in Zurich at a ripe old age[1]—has tremendous weight. Reflecting about Jewish fate in her book on

[1] 1874–1966.—Eds.

Job,[2] she writes about us: "He was our neighbor; we lived with him and loved him. What should be our attitude toward this horrible transformation? Forgiveness is for him who judges; ours is only a boundless, inexpungible sadness."

For even now that the devils have been put out of their murderous business, the dark desert of prejudice is still vast and wide. "It is in vain"—here is a voice of forty years ago, Jakob Wassermann's, but who can say that this voice is no longer valid?—"it is in vain to set an example in your life or behavior. They say: We know nothing, we have seen nothing, we have heard nothing. Vain to keep faith with them, as a comrade-in-arms or a fellow citizen. They say: He is Proteus, he can assume any shape or form. . . . Vain to live for them and die for them. They say: He is a Jew." [3]

It would take a separate investigation to set forth how the overcoming of prejudice should be tackled, what the small, laborious steps are like which are necessary and possible to keep in check semi-education, uncontrolled, stupid and brutish feelings, dreary generalizations. But it is certain that all understanding starts with knowledge, and surely no one can speak of knowledge among us. Not much has changed since the days when Franz Kafka said this in a conversation: "One can suppress one's fellow man much better if one does not know him. Then there are no pangs of conscience. That is why no one knows the history of the Jews." Gustav Janouch, with whom Kafka conversed in those days, protested: "That is not correct. Biblical history—that is, a portion of the history of the Jewish people—is taught in the very first grades in school." But Kafka —so we are informed—gave a bitter smile. "That's just it. In this way the history of the Jews is made to look like a fairy tale,

---

[2] *Das Buch Hiob und das Schicksal des jüdischen Volkes* (The Book of Job and the Fate of the Jewish People) (Zurich, 1946 and 1948).—Eds.

[3] From Wassermann's autobiographical work *My Life as German and Jew* (London: George Allen & Unwin Ltd., 1934), pp. 174–175; translator not indicated; originally published in Berlin in 1921 as *Mein Weg als Deutscher und Jude.*—Eds.

which a man later throws into the pit of oblivion together with his childhood." [4]

[2]

WHAT IS IT THAT WE DREDGE UP FROM THE "PIT OF OBLIVION"? The archetypes of Israel. We try to read in the age-old, multi-furrowed countenance: the darkness, the sadness, the clear light, the fire that suddenly flares up, the joy. Israel: That is Isaiah, Ezra, and Gamaliel—the voice of prophecy, the zeal of order, the patience in the council. It is also Chaim Weizmann, Walther Rathenau, and Martin Buber—the office of states-manlike responsibility and the authority of the great scholar.

Israel: The concentrated attention with which a people that knows words and has the power of language turns to the law. The scrolls record the law, but they want to be part of life; and only a combination of the two—the vested word and the di-rect, reshaping, surprising interpretation—forms an archetype of Israel, the judge.

Israel: The passionate love with which a tough, zealous, fes-tival-minded people turns to existence, the concern with life and health. "The dead praise not the Lord"—this anxious in-sight from its Book of Psalms constantly accompanied this people, together with a strong desire for vigor and a long life. "Live to be a hundred and twenty!"—this is what they wish one another, thus forming another archetype: the physician.

Israel: The incessant zeal to provide a place for the docu-ments entrusted to them, a dwelling place and permanence in the hearts of the scholars and their sons, with the certainty that the word dwells among us as voice, the voice of the messen-ger, the "resounding one," as truth in need of a person. Thus longing and loyalty produce a third archetype: the teacher.

[4] Gustav Janouch, *Gespräche mit Kafka* (Conversations with Kafka) (Frankfurt: Fischer Bücherei, 1961), pp. 75–76, as translated by the editors.

And only now shall we name the types which were bound to develop in the Diaspora because of exclusion from other professions: the merchant, the money-changer. And we know that the picture would not be a fair one if we did not speak of the Jewish peasant (I met one in Rumania)—of the well-versed craftsman whom our army hospitals in Eastern Europe employed because he was important to them, only to be killed by the men of the Security Service whenever they pleased—and they did please.[5] We have to mention the Jewish master builder—Gustav Oelsner's life is unforgotten by many of you —and since we are thinking of Jewish fellow citizens, we shall do well to name David Shaltiel, the general of the Israeli Army, the defender of Jerusalem in recent history, who sought and found the grave of his parents in Stellingen. We ought to speak of Jewish poets, especially those who managed to speak our language with a very special kind of love. Not many letters written in the German language are of the stature of Rosa Luxemburg's letters, and even in New Zealand Karl Wolfskehl had that everlasting part of Germany with him. I think of verses written by Gertrud Kolmar and of others which Nelly Sachs is writing in the German language in Stockholm.[6] And I am thinking of how a certain tone remained and still remains audible enough through all the shy and bold games of hide-and-seek, through all paths of irony and melancholia, a tone that is covert in Heine, but sounds open and unguarded in a verse of Rathenau: "Land, my land, my love!" [7]

[5] The Jewish craftsman to whom Goes refers here becomes Stefan in Goes's novella *The Boychik,* which we have included in this volume.—Eds.

[6] Since Goes delivered this address in 1962, Nelly Sachs (along with S. Y. Agnon) won the Nobel Prize for Literature in 1966.—Eds.

[7] From Walther Rathenau's poem "Die Stimme der Sehnsucht" (The Voice of Longing) from Rathenau's *Gesammelte Schriften* (Berlin: S. Fischer, 1925), Vol. I, p. 293.

[3]

BUT LET US NOT DELUDE OURSELVES. ALL THIS IS HARDLY AN EVO-
cation of images any more when it is done among us, but an
evocation of phantoms. We must listen to words which Leo
Baeck, the venerable head of the Jewish community in Berlin
and Theresienstadt, wrote in 1945. "For us Jews a historical
epoch has come to an end. Such an era comes to an end whenever a hope, a belief, a confidence must finally be buried. It
was our belief that the German and the Jewish spirit could
meet on German soil and that their marriage could produce a
blessing. That was an illusion. The epoch of the Jews in Germany is finished forever." Seventeen years have passed since
these words were written. By virtue of much subsequent evidence of hopeful love Leo Baeck may not have revoked them,
but he did—if I may say so—put parentheses around them. He
greeted us, the frightened and the awakened, without rancor
and in brotherhood. He has been dead for five years now. But
Martin Buber, too, who visited us occasionally in recent years,
has come as a guest—and how else would he be able to come?

The evocation of phantoms is a bleak undertaking. I do not
intend to do so here. Seeking the tone of joy, I have resolved to
comprehend anew the great vital words which Israel derived
from its prototypal influences, but also heard while simply existing in the world, and which it then actualized as one contribution, *its* contribution, to the history of the world spirit—as
words which are valid for us and which speak to us, in severity
and in kindness. I will interpret three guiding words here.
They are the words

GO   SUFFER   WAIT

[4]

ISRAEL'S HISTORY BEGAN WITH THE WORDS SPOKEN TO ABRAHAM IN
Genesis 12: "Go forth from thy native land and from thy kin-
dred, and thy father's house to a land that I will show thee."
There was a "Go!" over Jacob's path, and Moses obeyed God's
"Go" when in the Passover night he led the children of Israel
out of Egypt into the desert, toward Sinai, the mount of the
covenant, toward the promise "You shall be my people and I
will be your God." Here followed the "Go" from the days of
the prophet Jeremiah, Israel's way to the Babylonian captivity,
and seventy years later the command to return to the land
without a temple. After the destruction of Jerusalem there was
no end to the "Go"; the roads to the Diaspora all over the
earth opened up. It is a "Go" in which two things alternately
disappear from sight: Sometimes it is the point of departure,
and often enough it is the destination. "Perhaps one can still
get a visa for Venezuela"—this is what Stefan Zweig overheard
a man who was ready to go saying in a London office. And
another man answered, "But that is very far." Whereupon the
first man said, "Far? From where?" And then there were the
freight trains. In his report *If This Is a Man*,[8] one of the few
survivors, Primo Levi of Turin, has described for us the journey to Auschwitz—that "Go" with an almost unambiguous
destination. And finally, in 1948 and in the years since then,
the land of Israel, the State, the new homeland, became the
goal of a new "Go." What distinguishes this thousandfold
"Go" is expressed for the first time and for all times in Genesis
12: "Abraham went forth as the Lord had spoken to him." Let
no one euphemize here; like man in general, Israel has found
it hard to comprehend those obscure commands as God's directions, but it never completely disappeared from before their
eyes, this sure image of God's presence. "Treu dem ewigen
Bunde/ Ziehe immer wieder, wieder immer/ Vor euch, tags

[8] (Se questo è un uomo), trans. by Stuart Woolf (New York: Orion Press,
1959).

Gewölk and nächtens Schimmer/ Nächtens Schimmer!" [9] The
people of Israel had the secret of the Ark of the Covenant: the
certainty that they, constant wanderers who hurriedly drove
their tent pegs into the ground for a short sojourn, were carrying with them the law of their God, the gift of the Word, of the
Word alone, of the blessing, of the quickly given and quickly
taken coin of the Word as the property of the fugitives of God.
Other peoples live between the walls of durability, like Greece
and Rome; others have the epic of the long breath or the picture galleries of visible permanence. When Israel celebrates, it
celebrates its "Go" in the night of liberation, it thinks of the
bread of affliction and bitter herbs, and the youngest at the
table asks, "Why is this night different from all other nights?"
If, in all this, *poverty* is their lot, it is the poverty of someone
who can be light, who is capable of traveling light. When one
of the sons, the writer Albrecht Schaeffer,[10] left from the port of
Hamburg in 1939, there was a reminiscence of Abraham's
"Go":

> "Gehe, weil du Füsse hast zu gehen.
> Nirgends sollst du weilen auf der Erde.
> Bis sich Haupt und Glieder niederlegen
> Trage bei dir nichts als meinen Segen.
> Sorge, dass dein Wandel richtig werde
> Und ich werde milde auf dich sehen.
>
> Trage bei dir nichts als meinen Segen." [11]

Four years later, however, in the cellars of Berlin, in the
hiding places of those who had disappeared, the basic text—so
we are told—was the word of prophecy about Job which told

[9] "True to my eternal covenant I pace before you again and again, as a
cloud by day and as fire by night, by night as fire." From Karl Wolfskehl's
poem "Am Seder zu sagen" (To be Said at the Seder).

[10] *Non*-Jewish poet, novelist, and dramatist, 1885–1950.—Eds.

[11] Go because you have feet to walk on. Nowhere shall you tarry on
earth. Until your head and your limbs lie down, carry nothing on you but
my blessing. See to it that you lead a proper life and I shall look upon
you charitably. Carry nothing on you but my blessing."

him who had nothing that he lacked nothing: "He allures thee out of distress into a broad place, where there is no straitness."

What does it mean—so we must ask—if this "Go" spoken to Israel is now seriously addressed to us, the Germans of today and present-day Christendom? I have no political function here; if I did, I would ask some questions of all those who, making promises which cannot possibly be meant sincerely, speak of old boundaries, flags, and ensigns. It is enough that we call worry and unrest our good counsellors—and they *are* our good counsellors—that we get frightened in all realms in which we discover ourselves marking time. Anyone who is incapable of wanting more than "to have and to hold" will have a new edifice today, but a ruin the day after tomorrow; then he will have nothing but a rampart with loopholes, and shortly thereafter a bunker into which he must crawl and lock himself up. He will have to enter into an alliance with two not very good forces: security by dint of which alien influences are repulsed; and power, by dint of which everything alien is combated. It may be that this is how one preserves one's bunker called life; but the potential and the happiness of an evolving life are not gained in that fashion. To hear the "Go" would probably mean a dual ability: to accept and to let go, to preserve and not to preserve.

[5]

SUFFER! WITH THE MARK OF SUFFERING AND A WRENCHED HIP SOCKET, Israel—as reported in Genesis 32—entered into its own personality, into the history of its name ("Wrestler with God"); and in the "servant of God," as presented to the people and to the peoples in Isaiah 53, in the image of one who bears another's sufferings and accepts tribulation, it recognized its destiny. This consciousness penetrated even the history of Hasidism in the 18th century. There we read: "It is known that the Great Maggid used crutches. . . . He *was* perfect and . . . with each of his limbs he moves all the worlds, as it is written in the Book of Splendor: 'Mercy—that is the right arm, rigor is the left.' That was why he dragged his left foot. He offered it up, lest he waken rigor within the world." [12] It was Israel's concern not to arouse violence and not to meet untrammeled violence with force. Israel was familiar with the sad realization that God's glory manifests itself in this world in veiled form— as a judge, an afflicter, a beggar. In the history of its alien status in the world, Israel has never entirely lost sight of the consciousness of having been appointed to this task, and there has never been a lack of great realizations. When in the Spring of 1945 the liberators came to Theresienstadt, it so happened that for a few days the tormentors were in the power of the prisoners. We know that in those days no harm came to the erstwhile "supervisors," because—Leo Baeck was present in the camp. Such was the radiance that emanated from a man who had *really* heard the words "Do not avenge yourselves!"

In their readiness to turn passiveness into activity these people became helpers and teachers for one another and for the nations among which they lived—often enough without knowing what was taking place. "Strange! People come to see me who are beset by melancholia," wrote the Rabbi of Lublin, "and when they go hence they are illuminated even though I myself—" here he was going to say "am melancholy", but he interrupted himself and said instead "am dark and do not shine." And what bright light shines for us, centuries after Shylock's "Sufferance is the badge of all our tribe," from the defenseless smile with which a terrible answer in life's game of dice was given in 1943 or thereabouts. "Jew," said the commandant of a concentration camp, "you know that you are not going to get out of here alive. But I shall give you a chance. Listen. I have a glass eye . . . the best glass eye that was ever made; it can't be told apart from a real eye. If you can guess

[12] Martin Buber, *Tales of the Hasidim: Early Masters,* translated by Olga Marx (New York: Schocken Books, 1961), p. 112.

which of my eyes is of glass, I shall let you live." And the man thus addressed looked up briefly and said, "The right one." "I'll be damned! You guessed it. My right eye is a glass eye. But tell me, Jew, how did you guess?" "If you will pardon me for saying so, Herr Kommandant, there's such a kindly look in your right eye." All the depths of melancholia, irony, self-irony, which, as you know, are part and parcel of Jewish humor, are rolled up in this "If you will pardon me, Herr Kommandant"—not as the tricks of the victor who lands on his feet, something that may be germane to Turkish humor or to the *Arabian Nights,* but as the bittersweet consolation of the lowly.

This people became receptive to the world and pervious to fate when it knew enough to accept its Job-word "Suffer." It seemed destined to understand those it was facing, to interpret alien things—as translators and interpreters, as grateful care-takers. You may be thinking of Friedrich Gundolf or Bruno Walter, and I am also thinking of the visitors from Rehovoth who came to Württemberg, their childhood home. I can still see the gesture with which they took Johann Sebastian Bach's Fourth Brandenburg Concerto out of the record cabinet, the gesture of joy: "May we listen to the third movement? Those three general pauses at the end . . . they are like a window to eternity." And later one of them took a volume of Goethe poems from my shelf, and with complete familiarity he turned to what he wanted to show me. They had told me of their mountains in Israel, the early morning light there, and then one of them had said: "But, you know, I am not satisfied with just seeing it; I should also like to be able to tell about it. But—what else can I say? Here it has already been said—and for all times." Whereupon he read, shaking with awe, a line from the *Westöstlicher Divan:* "Wenn am Gebirg der Morgen sich entzündet . . ." (When the morning is inflamed by the mountains . . .)

But as for us—how does this archetypal word obligate us? First, surely, through our participation. We invoke things that have happened: that mound of children's shoes and the smell of the excrement, the even-tempered clattering of the typewriters on which the murder lists were prepared . . . not in order to perpetuate grief, but only for the sake of staying alert. "The womb is fertile yet from which that crawled" [13]—the disquieting final outcry of our moralists forbids us the sleep of forgetfulness.

Permit someone who prefers to say what he deems it necessary to say in a poem of his own and who mounts the lecture platform only occasionally to return to his real world and to remember there the undetachable chain which has been placed around our generation's neck. Into the warmest memories of childhood, the paths of love, the landscape of our joy, there penetrates the truth about the world in which we live:

When we were swinging in the tree of life,
—Do you remember, my brother—
And mother called out our names
Right up to the tree top, brother,
She probably thought that a fight awaited us,
For she too, the brave woman,
Knew how to fight;
Sweet and mild and close
Was the smell of the apple tree
Around St. James's Day,
Bitter was the aroma
Of the nut tree.
The table and the bench were prepared,
The boys learned a lot:
Languages and geography and history
And the Pythagorean theorem.
But not yet one theorem:
NUT-TREE WOOD IS GOOD FOR GUNSTOCKS.

Later came Plane Tree Alley,
And we guided the boats,
Relaxing now, to the
Dark greenery by the Hölderlin Tower.

[13] Bert Brecht, *The Resistable World of Arturo Ui.*

Your voices were with us:
Rachel, Susanna—
Your names:
Rachel, Susanna—
Cheerful for you, brother,
But sorrowful for me
And secretly beloved.
Pretty, provisional names.
And no one had told us
THE DEFINITIVE COLLECTIVE NAME ANNE FRANK.

But now
When the quince-tree leaves
Suggest to us happiness and bliss,
The innocence of living creatures,
Even in November's light—
To whom belongs that last forgotten fruit
There in the tree top?
Rachel, Susanna, my brother in the tree of life—
Now, to be sure, our necks are choked
By the undetachable chain:
TREE FRUIT FRUIT CORE PRUSSIC ACID AUSCHWITZ.

Participation—that is what I called our response to the archetypal word "Suffer." Participation is not something rapturous; it is sobriety, alertness, attentiveness—in particular that attentiveness which is open to the other in its multifarious guises.

You, my Hamburg audience, had a special lesson to learn during the past weeks; it does not behoove a visitor to join in the discussion. I believe we have learned all over again what the countenance of a man who is truly able to help men looks like: It is a face from which stubbornness, cocksureness, the worshiping of success, rigidity, and a pedantic clinging to principles increasingly vanish to give way to other, greater, realities: astonishment, the ability to be frightened, defenselessness, reverence, awe, gratitude.

[6]

"WAIT!" IS THE THIRD OF THE ARCHETYPAL WORDS WITH WHICH
we are concerned here. Israel's history is marked by a *futurum
divinum,* by the blessing which was pronounced over Abraham
—"I will bless you and you shall be a blessing"—and which
subsequently assumed the concrete form of promise in the
mouths of the patriarchs and the judges, the kings and the
prophets: the blessed people, all generations of which are
blessed; the chosen people, the radiance of God over Zion; the
root of Jesse; the Messianic kingdom of peace. Israel's circui-
tous and wrong paths are not glossed over in the Scripture; the
Prophets more than anyone else are Israel's most severe
preachers of penitence. But the covenant is maintained and
the promise is believed in. "I wait for your deliverance, o
Lord!"—these words of the dying Jacob are also Simeon's
words in the Temple of Jerusalem, the songs of Yehuda
Halevi, and the light on the way for the Baal-Shem-Tov, the
father of Hasidism. Theodor Herzl translated them into his
language, the language of Zionist longing—nay, of Zionist passion; and when, in the Warsaw Ghetto, those locked in a burning building had time only for one last "Hear, o Israel!" their
souls still remained open to the future: "I wait for your deliverance, o Lord!"

In the course of time the focal points have changed and mul-
tiplied. The image of the Messiah who is called "Wonderful,
Counsellor, the Mighty God, the Everlasting Father, the
Prince of Peace" mingled with the longing for the Messianic
realm. To the great patience of the pious there was added the
impatience of those pressing on, and not at every moment of
Israel's history as the history of those who waited could Messianic and pseudo-Messianic expectations be clearly separated
(Martin Buber has described an exciting epoch of intermin-
gling in his *Gog und Magog* [*For the Sake of Heaven*]); and
even Israel's most recent history, the history of the State of Israel, is not and cannot be a "smoothly written book."

Yet a threefold characteristic distinguishes this "Wait" in Israel. In this "Wait" the secret of a wonderful composure is alive. As Israel says "Now, at this moment," it says at the same time "Three thousand years or more." "It is there," said Martin Buber, remembering the dead in the old cemetery in Worms. "It is there for me, not as corporeality within the space of this planet, but as corporeality deep in my own memories, back into the depths of history, back as far as Sinai. I have stood there; I have been united with the ashes and through them with the patriarchs. That is a remembrance of the divine-human encounter which is granted to all Jews." In the same vein Richard Beer-Hofmann writes in his poem "Lullaby for Miriam":

> "Deep in us flows
> Blood of our forebears to meet those to come,
> Blood of our fathers so restless and proud.
> In us are *all*. Who feels he is alone?"

This is the first characteristic. But in this "Wait" there lies also the dignity of steadfastness in time. The goal does not make Israel forget the road; over the prospect it does not forget the time, the hour, this day. "If not now, when?"—this question of the great Rabbi Hillel has made the Jews, the people of faith, efficient in time; the figure of Victor Gollancz comes to mind here. And even their mystics, if I may term the Hasidic movement thus—especially they, did not permit any escape from time; in the ritual bath, by the baking oven, in the conversation between draymen is the hour of the eternal. "If not now, when?"

And finally, this "Wait" contains the splendor of unspent life. Think of the faces of the old Jews as painted by Rembrandt, of Marc Chagall's rabbis, or of a face of our time like that of Lise Meitner. Are these faces old? Yes, thousands of years old, the contemporaries of Jacob and Rachel. But we could also say, considering their earnest patience and their faith, that the dominant feature of these faces is not old age but that youth which, with touching inaccuracy, we call "eternal youth."

Those who take this "Wait" to heart—here, now, and among us—will be afraid of living for the present without a sense of history; they will guard against forgetting their past, for better or for worse. He who does not remember does not think. He who does not live *with* his past lives like a gnat at dusk.

But at the same time, to be sure, those addressed here are frightened at the possibility that they might be paralyzed by this very past, by the weight of tradition, unfit for a changing world which, after all, asks us to be ready for new communication in an almost new language and with a new joyousness.

Finally: What matters is to find out that someone who is filled with concern about his external well-being is vouchsafed the fulfillment of his wishes, but that these fulfilled wishes are accompanied by fatigue and boredom. "May your old age be like your youth": That is a Biblical promise which comes to life only over tasks of the spirit and of kindness, tasks which no one completes before his dying day.

[7]

TO CONCLUDE BY RETURNING TO THE BEGINNING: WE ARE NOT LIKE the man outside the door who listens, examines, and misses a sound. We are inside the room; we are present; we are partners and have our parts. Where is our place? I spoke about Martin Buber's walk through the Jewish cemetery of Worms. And here are his words, spoken thirty years ago, like a farewell: "I live a short distance from the city of Worms, to which I am also tied by ancestral tradition; and from time to time I visit there. When I do so, I always go first to the cathedral. It is a visible harmony of members, a whole in which no part deviates from the norm of perfection. I walk around the cathedral, gazing at it in perfect joy. Then I go to the Jewish cemetery. It consists of cracked and crooked stones without shape or direction. I enter the cemetery and look up from this disorder to the marvelous harmony of the cathedral, and it seems to me as if I were looking from Israel up to the Church. . . . I have stood there and I have experienced everything myself. I have experienced all the death that was before me; all the ashes, all the desolation, and all the noiseless wailings become mine. But the covenant has not been withdrawn from me. I lie on the ground, prostrate like these stones. But it has not been withdrawn for me." [14]

It is uncertain whether the " 'Patriarch' from Jerusalem," the man who combines human joy at a finished work with the deeper religious joy at the non-wavering covenant, will walk that road again in his lifetime. But we, so it seems to me, have been called onto this road.

Those who come from the cathedral have their "Praised be Jesus Christ" and have received greetings not as a weapon but as the mark of the joy with which a man is able to see his fellow man—because he simultaneously sees the image of the Son of Man, man as God intended him.

Those who come from the cemetery have their "Shalom," the greeting of peace—and *if* they have it, there and for us, it is, after all the history of guilt that also lies buried in this cemetery, not a casual greeting but a real one, the greeting of overcoming and forgiveness.

This is not the place to set forth what will follow this greeting in the conversation between minds, the long spiritual silence between Christianity and Judaism having ended about forty years ago, or what form the question as to truth—without any syncretistic way out—will now take for the conversers.

[14] From *Christianity: Some Non-Christian Appraisals* edited by David McKain. Copyright 1964 by David W. McKain. Used by permission of the publishers, McGraw-Hill Book Company. The full text of Buber's remarks on the Jewish cathedral and Goes's response to them will be found in this volume on pp. 220–221

Since there are *two* givers and *two* takers, it will not be a meager conversation.

And even though there may be some among us who do not feel authorized to use either of the two greetings, neither "Blessed be Jesus Christ" nor "Shalom," the words which "everyone should repeat immediately" are obligatory for all of us. "What everyone should repeat immediately"—this is Franz Werfel's heading for verses which he wrote in 1917 and which begin with these lines:

> Never again
> Will I deride a human face.

To conclude: Between the shadow of the cathedral stones and the shade of the old cemetery trees, where men seek their way, with underided faces and called by this GO, SUFFER, WAIT, called in a tone of serious joy, there, my listeners, is the place of all of us.

Albrecht Goes ✡ IN MEMORIAM MARTIN BUBER

Born in Vienna, February 8, 1878
Died in Jerusalem, June 13, 1965

AT NOON ON JUNE 13, 1965, WHEN NEWS OF MARTIN BUBER'S death went out, there were untold numbers of people on all continents who felt this death as a personal loss; a world without Martin Buber is to them a poorer and colder world. And in reflecting upon the irretrievable loss of a great personality, many of them probably recalled the last story Buber told about the Rabbi of Berdichev—it is entitled "Since Then" and reads like this:

Since the death of Rabbi Levi Yitzhak there has no longer been a rabbi in Berdichev. The congregation has not been able to find anyone to fill the place he left empty.[1]

The story should not be interpreted as meaning "That was a Caesar! When will his equal appear?" It should rather be interpreted this way: The congregation, which had comprehended who its rabbi really had been, carried on with its Sabbaths and workdays, its prayers, its communal life, and its celebrations, without him, but in such as manner *as if he were*

[1] *Tales of the Hasidim: Early Masters*, p. 234.

276

there. The life of the messenger comes to an end, but his mission does not end. And thus it is here too; a place is empty, but those who know who is missing here are not to lament passively and brood about this empty place.

It is quite possible that in the future many people will read the "Scriptures translated into German by Martin Buber" without paying much attention to the name of the translator; that they will commune with Levi Yitzhak and Zusya of Hanipol, Rabbi Shmelke and Moshe Leib, indeed with all the insights in *I and Thou* without knowing to whom they are indebted for all of this; and it is very likely that no "Martin Buber System" will survive. But one hardly needs more than an hour's time with Buber's autobiographical fragments— called *Meetings*[2]—to be certain of what it is in Buber that will last. What will not be forgotten is the image of the teacher who was able to confirm by the truth of his life his insights into what was truth; not—and this is his own distinction—as a "seer," but as a "seeing person"; not as one of those thirty-six righteous men on which, according to an old Jewish legend, the world and its continuance rests, but, rather, as one who— relentlessly dissipating the fog of illusion, particularly the fog of pious illusion—confronts those entrusted to him with the eternal Thou—"No place without Him"; as one who expects nothing less from his companion than that he "be available," that he "give himself to the task." Nothing less than this—to close with one of his bold, precise formulations: "that the customary soul enlarges and transfigures itself into the surprise soul." [3]

[2] In English in *The Philosophy of Martin Buber,* Vol. XII of *The Library of Living Philosophers,* edited by Paul Arthur Schilpp and Maurice Friedman (La Salle, Illinois: Open Court, 1967), pp. 3–39.

[3] "Prophecy, Apocalyptic, and the Historical Hour," in Martin Buber, *Pointing the Way,* translated, edited, and with a new introduction by Maurice S. Friedman (New York: Harper Torchbooks, 1963), p. 206.

SELECTED BIBLIOGRAPHY

FITZELL, JOHN. "Albrecht Goes: The Poet as Spiritual Guest."
Monatshefte, L, No. 7 (December, 1958), 348–358.
   Fitzell sees Goes as a poet who has supped at many tables but al-
ways as a guest who moves on.
FRIEDMAN, MAURICE S. *Martin Buber: Encounter on the Narrow
Ridge.* New York: McGraw-Hill Book Company, 1969.
   One of Buber's encounters on the narrow ridge was his en-
counter with Albrecht Goes.
———. *Martin Buber: The Life of Dialogue.* Harper Torchbooks.
New York: Harper & Row, Publishers, 1960.
   The most comprehensive study of Buber's thought in English;
includes a bibliography of works by and on Buber through 1960.
KORNFELD, ANITA R. "Albrecht Goes, Pastor-Poet: An Introduction."
Unpublished honors thesis. Waltham, Massachusetts: Department
of European Languages and Literature, Brandeis University, 1961.
   A mature and sensitive study of Goes's works with emphasis on
their relationship to Buber.
ROLLINS, E. WILLIAM. "Albrecht Goes, Man of Dialogue: The Personal and Literary Relationship of Goes to Martin Buber." Unpublished dissertation. Nashville, Tennessee: Department of Ger-
manic and Slavic Languages, Vanderbilt University, 1968. (Available on microfilm through University Microfilms, Ann Arbor,
Michigan.)
   A detailed study of Goes's relationship to Buber; includes a
bibliography of all works by and on Albrecht Goes.

SCHAEDER, GRETE. *Martin Buber: Hebräischer Humanismus.* Göttingen: Vandenhoeck & Ruprecht, 1966.

The most comprehensive work on Buber in German.

SCHILPP, PAUL ARTHUR, AND FRIEDMAN, MAURICE, EDS. *The Philosphy of Martin Buber.* Vol. XII of *The Library of Living Philosophers.* La Salle, Illinois: Open Court; London: Cambridge University Press, 1967.

A symposium on Buber's thought by a wide range of scholars, followed by Buber's reply to them; also includes Buber's "Autobiographical Fragments" and a full bibliography of his writings.

ZOHN, HARRY. "A Novel of Expiation." *The Reconstructionist,* XXIII, No. 2 (March 8, 1957), 26–27.

A review of Albrecht Goes's *The Burnt Offering.*

INDEX